SOURCE BOOK OF HEALTH INSURANCE DATA

1991

CONTENTS

TABLES

CHAPTER 5

PREFACE

The *Source Book of Health Insurance Data 1991* is the thirty-first consecutive edition of this report, which has been published annually by HIAA since 1960.

A statistical report of private health insurance in the United States, the *Source Book* is compiled by HIAA's Department of Policy Development and Research. The report provides the latest available data on the major forms of health insurance coverage, medical care costs, utilization of the nation's medical facilities, and national morbidity trends. It also contains new and updated information on health care and health care fields, incorporating new facts about managed health care. Expanded sections on medical care costs and utilization data also have been added.

The data found in the *Source Book* are taken from reports of insurance companies, government agencies, hospital and medical associations, and other health insurance plans.

The *Source Book* is meant to be a basic reference tool for writers, editors, researchers, educators, government leaders, hospital and medical professionals, members of business associations, and others interested in the health care industry.

HIAA hopes that this thirty-first edition proves as valuable as its predecessors.

Richard E. Curtis
Director, Department of Policy Development and Research

Chapter 1

THE ROLE AND FUNCTION OF HEALTH INSURANCE

Health insurance provides people with a way to protect themselves against financial catastrophe and to assure themselves and their families of access to the health care system.

In 1850, The Accidental Death Association of London was the first company to offer coverage for medical expense for bodily injuries that did not result in death. In the United States at the end of that same year, the Franklin Health Assurance Company of Massachusetts offered the same type coverage. Ten years later, The Travelers Insurance Company of Hartford began offering medical expense coverage on a basis resembling health insurance in its present form. By 1866, health insurance policies were being written by 60 other insurance companies.

At the beginning of the twentieth century, both accident insurance companies and life insurance companies were writing health insurance policies. The early policies were essentially loss-of-income policies and provided benefits for a limited number of diseases such as typhus, typhoid, scarlet fever, smallpox, diphtheria, and diabetes.

◆ The Beginnings of Modern Health Insurance

The birth of modern health insurance came in 1929, when a group of school teachers made a contract with Baylor Hospital in Dallas, Texas, to provide room, board, and specified ancillary services at a predetermined monthly cost. This plan generally is acknowledged as the first of what came to be called Blue Cross plans. The Blue Cross plans were attractive not only to consumers but also to hospitals because they needed to find a mechanism to assure that patients would be able to pay for services they provided. For patients who were covered by the Blue Cross plan, payment was made directly from the plan to the hospital, rather than reimbursing the patient who would then pay the hospital. Coverage under the Blue Cross policies was typically for a hospital stay of a specified number of days or for particular hospital services. These plans contrasted with the indemnity plans offered by private insurance carriers which reimbursed (that is, "indemnified") the patient for covered services up to a specified dollar limit. It was up to the hospital to collect the money from the patient. Blue Shield plans, initiated by physicians, followed and were based on similar concepts except they offered coverage for physician services. The Blue Cross and Blue Shield plans traditionally established premiums by community rating; that is, everybody in the community paid the same premium.

Starting in the 1930s and continuing into the war years, traditional insurance companies began to add health insurance coverage for hospital, surgical, and medical expenses to their accident and life insurance lines of business. During World War II group health insurance became an attractive benefit to workers at a time when wages were frozen. The trend was strengthened by the favorable tax treatment that fringe benefits received. Unlike money wages, they were not subject to income or Social Security taxes, so a dollar of health insurance was worth more than an after-tax dollar spent out of pocket for medical services. Health insurance quickly became a benefit that was covered by the collective bargaining contracts of employee groups. Its position as a permanent part of employee benefits was assured in the postwar era when the Supreme Court ruled that employee benefits, including health insurance, were a legitimate part of the labor-management bargaining process.

Although early policies were often sufficiently broad to cover the expenses of common accidents and illnesses, they were inadequate to cover extended illnesses or long hospital stays. To correct this deficiency, in the early 1950s insurers began to offer major medical expense insurance to cover catastrophic cases. Soon thereafter, Blue Cross-Blue Shield followed the lead of the private insurers and offered similar plans. Typically the policyholder under major medical expense insurance paid a specified deductible amount after which the insured and the insurer shared the covered losses according to a specified ratio (coinsurance).

During the 1950s, health insurance protection expanded rapidly and by the middle of the decade 77 million people had hospital expense insurance in either the indemnity form or under a major medical plan.

In the next few years, insurance companies began to offer a new high-benefit major medical plan, which encompassed "out-of-pocket" cutoff points beyond which the insurance company paid 100 percent of covered expenses.

These same types of health insurance plans, expanded in coverage to meet new medical technology, are in wide use today.

◆Medicare and Medicaid

During the next 20 years, health insurance would not only continue to cover an increasing number of people, but also greatly broaden the scope of its coverage. The federal government's Medicare program for people over the age of 65 became effective July 1, 1966.

For the portion of the working population covered by Social Security, it provided compulsory hospitalization insurance (Part A) as well as voluntary supplementary medical insurance (Part B) to help pay for physicians' services, medical services, and supplies not covered by the hospitalization plan. To fill gaps in Medicare coverage, nearly 23 million, or 70 percent of Medicare enrollees, supplement their Medicare benefits with private insurance policies.

Medicaid, designed to share the cost of medical care for low-income people, also became effective in 1966 under Title 19 of the Social Security Act. It allowed states to add health coverage, with federal matching funds, to their public assistance programs for low-income groups, families with dependent children, the aged, and the disabled. Because eligibility is based upon meeting criteria in addition to having a low income, only 40 percent of the population living below the poverty line is covered by the Medicaid program today.

◆Recent Changes

Private insurance companies continued to determine premiums through actuarial assessments of the risk associated with the insured group, and premiums would differ from group to group because the risk of groups varied. In other words, groups' premiums were based on their own medical claims experience, later known as experience rating. It was only a short step from experience rating to self-insurance. Some big companies realized that their work force was large enough that aggregate medical experience and expenses of their employees would vary little from year to year (except for inflation in medical prices). Given such predictability of medical experience and expense, it was feasible for large companies to self-insure. Rather than pay insurers a premium to bear the risk, the employer could simply assume the risk by budgeting a certain amount to pay claims. In addition, the firm could retain control over funds until the time a medical bill needed to be paid.

Two other factors related to government regulations spurred self-insurance. In virtually all states, insurance companies had to pay a premium tax of several percentage points, the cost of which was passed on to customers. Self-insured firms could avoid this cost. In addition, states began mandating that insurance policies cover certain specified services and the services of particular provider groups. But the Employee Retirement Income Security Act of 1974 (ERISA) prohibited states from applying these mandates to self-insured plans. Thus employers who did not want to pay the extra costs of these mandated benefits (now nearly 900 when aggregated across all states) could avoid doing so by self-insuring. The combination of these factors led to rapid growth of self-insurance in the mid-to-late 1970s. Employers often turned to insurers to administer plans through administrative-services-only (ASO) contracts; self-insurance became a dominant form of group coverage. Currently the various kinds of plans in which the employer group assumes all or a substantial portion of the risk account for 55 percent of total commercial health insurance business, with ASO arrangements accounting for 31 percent, and minimum premium plans and stop-loss plans accounting for another 24 percent.

Once self-insurance became an option, community rating was no longer a viable way of determining premiums for groups that were large enough to self-insure with the exception of some very large accounts that stayed in federally qualified HMOs and continued to practice community rating. It would be advantageous for any group of below-average risk to leave the "community" in which it was paying a premium that reflected the risk of the total community, including those of higher risk than itself, and self-insure. As a consequence, in recent years, not just private insurance carriers but also Blue Cross-Blue Shield plans have been forced to turn to experience rating as the predominant method of premium rating for the types of groups that have the option of self-insuring.

◆ The Increasing Visibility of Managed Care

As health care costs rose drastically in the 1970s and 1980s, attention turned to new delivery systems, initially health maintenance organizations (HMOs) and later preferred provider organizations (PPOs) and other hybrid arrangements. These health care delivery systems (now called managed care) seemed to offer the potential for controlling costs by organizing providers into coherent networks and by integrating the financing and delivery of medical care. In such plans, mechanisms assure the coordination of a broad range of patient services and monitor care to determine that it is appropriate and delivered in the most efficient and inexpensive way.

At the beginning of 1991, between 50 million and 60 million persons were enrolled in HMOs, PPOs, exclusive provider organizations, and point-of-service plans. Growth of managed care can be expected to continue as new permutations on existing models develop.

Managed care companies now are developing specialty networks for mental health, vision, dental, chiropractic, podiatric, and physical therapy care. Sophisticated managed care principles also are being applied to other medically re-

lated fields, such as long-term care, and medical bills associated with auto liability and Workers' Compensation claims.

◆ Major Trends in Coverage, Utilization, and Expenditure

From its beginning, the emphasis of health care reimbursement has been on
hospital coverage, since the hospital has been the center of medical technology and since it claims the largest share of medical expense dollars. As the
scope of health insurance grew and health insurance policies found a niche in
the financial plans of the majority of Americans, the dramatic progress of surgical techniques and technology, along with their increasing costs, encouraged a
demand for surgical coverage. By the 1950s, nearly 60 million people had surgical expense insurance.

A growing realization that physician care is critical to good health encouraged
21 million people in the 1950s to purchase insurance coverage for physicians'
medical fees as well as for surgery. By 1989, Americans spent $56 billion on
physicians' services through private insurance.

During the 1950s and 1960s, most health insurance policies sold by insurance
companies contained the three basic coverages for health insurance: hospital
care, surgical fees, and related physicians' services.

Anticipating the requirements of the insurance-buying public, insurance companies began offering in the 1970s more comprehensive coverages and increased benefit levels that ranged from $50,000 to several million dollars un-
der comprehensive major medical expense policies.

In 1989, public and private health insurance protected 214 million Americans,
but more than 31 million persons, many employed by firms that do not offer
coverage, were still without health insurance coverage. Many of these people
without coverage were poor but still did not qualify for Medicaid.

Commercial insurance companies, Blue Cross-Blue Shield plans, self-funded
employer plans, and prepayment plans (such as HMOs) cover 90 percent of
the people who purchase private coverage. During 1989 these private programs paid more than $185 billion for health care expenses.

Hospital services are also an important factor in determining a large proportion of physician expenses and it became imperative that insurers, both public
and private, primarily concern themselves with monitoring the use and costs
of hospital services.

In 1990, Americans spent $666.2 billion ($384 billion in private funds and
$283 billion in public funds) for medical and health care services, research,

and construction of medical facilities. Private insurance companies spent nearly $186 billion on personal health care, a $17 billion increase over the previous year.

Rising health care costs continue to be the most pressing problem of the health care system. In 1969, per capita expenditures for health care were $268 in this country. By 1990, the figure had increased to $2,567. During the same 20-year period, health expenditures grew from 5.3 percent of the gross national product (GNP) to 12.2 percent.

There are three leading reasons for health care cost escalation: (1) increases in coverage have raised levels of expectation and demand; (2) incentives for providers and consumers have encouraged high levels of utilization, discouraged cost consciousness, and created tolerance for inefficiency and provision of marginally useful care; and (3) new technologies have usually brought improvements in quality at substantial increases in the cost of treating an episode of illness.

Many important facts about health care coverage, claims payments, services, and expenditures are summarized in Table 1.1.

Table 1.1

Key Health Insurance Statistics

	1985	1986	1987	1988	1989	1990	Percent change 1988–1989	Percent change 1989–1990
Persons with and without health care coverage*(millions)								
Total population	235.5	238.2	240.5	243.1	247.9	NA	0.7	NA
Persons with public and private coverage	204.2	204.7	208.7	211.6	216.6	NA	0.9	NA
Private health insurance	180.1	180.1	181.1	188.4	189.0	NA	0.3	NA
Employer-related	147.1	145.8	146.7	153.3	153.8	NA	0.3	NA
Persons without coverage	31.3	33.5	31.8	31.5	31.3	NA	−0.6	NA
Private health insurance claims payments(billions)**								
Total†	$ 117.6	$ 128.5	$ 151.7	$ 171.1	$ 185.3	NA	8.3	NA
Insurance companies	59.9	64.3	72.5	83.0	89.4	NA	7.7	NA
Blue Cross-Blue Shield	37.5	40.6	44.5	48.2	50.7	NA	5.2	NA
Other plans†	32.5	36.8	56.5	62.8	99.8	NA	27.1	NA
Private health insurance payment by category of service*(billions)**								
Total	$ 134.1	$ 143.5	$ 156.3	$ 174.4	$ 196.4	$ 216.8	12.6	10.4
Hospital care	59.5	63.8	69.5	75.4	83.2	89.4	10.3	7.5
Physicians' services	33.7	38.3	43.9	49.1	52.8	58.2	7.5	10.2
Dentists' services	9.1	9.9	11.0	12.4	13.5	15.1	8.9	11.9
Other professional services‡	5.2	6.1	7.5	8.9	10.6	12.8	19.1	20.8
Drugs and medical nondurables	5.2	5.5	6.0	6.5	7.3	8.3	12.3	13.7
Vision products and other medical durables	0.7	0.8	0.9	1.0	1.2	1.3	20.0	8.3
Home health care	0.3	0.3	0.3	0.3	0.4	0.5	33.3	25.0
Nursing home care	0.3	0.3	0.4	0.5	0.5	0.6	0.0	20.0
Program administration and cost of private health insurance	20.0	18.2	16.9	20.3	26.8	30.7	32.0	14.6
National health expenditures*(billions)**								
National health expenditures***	$ 422.6	$ 454.9	$ 494.1	$ 546.0	$ 602.8	$ 666.2	10.4	10.5
Health services and supplies	407.2	438.9	476.8	526.2	582.1	643.4	10.6	10.5
All private funds	247.7	264.6	285.7	318.9	350.2	383.6	9.8	9.5
All public funds	174.8	190.2	208.4	227.1	252.6	282.6	11.2	11.9
National health expenditures as percent of GNP	10.5	10.7	10.9	11.2	11.6	12.2	2.0	5.2
Per capita national health expenditures, private and public	$1,710	$1,822	$1,961	$2,146	$2,346	$2,566	9.3	9.4
Private funds	1,003	1,060	1,134	1,253	1,363	1,478	8.8	8.4
Public funds	707	762	827	893	983	1,089	10.1	10.8

SOURCES: *U.S. Bureau of the Census, Current Population Survey.
 **Health Insurance Association of America, Source Book Survey.
 ***Health Care Financing Administration, National Health Expenditure Accounts.
†Other plans include self-insured plans, self-administered plans, plans employing third-party administrators, and health maintenance organizations.
‡Other professional services include fees for chiropractors, podiatrists, psychologists, therapists, audiologists, optometrists, portable X-ray suppliers, ambulance service suppliers, and free-standing ESRD facilities.

Chapter 2

THE PRIVATE HEALTH INSURANCE INDUSTRY

◆ Coverage

At the end of 1989, nearly 214 million Americans or 87 percent of the civilian noninstitutionalized population, were protected by health care coverage according to the Current Population Survey by the Bureau of the Census. (Table 2.1)

Private health insurance with commercial insurance companies, Blue Cross-Blue Shield plans, self-funded employer plans, and prepayment plans such as HMOs covered 189 million persons.

The 1990 HIAA survey of commercial insurance companies found that almost 96 million persons were insured under group policies and nearly 10 million persons carried individual or family policies. (Table 2.2)

Most commercial health insurance companies provide two basic categories of coverage: medical expense insurance and disability income insurance. Medical expense insurance provides broad benefits that can cover virtually all expenses connected with hospital and medical care and related services. Disability income insurance provides periodic payments when the insured is unable to work as a result of sickness or injury.

Blue Cross-Blue Shield nonprofit membership plans serve state and regional areas and offer both individual and group health insurance coverage. The Blue Cross-Blue Shield Association coordinates the Blue Cross-Blue Shield plans of the nation.

Health care coverage also is provided through HMOs offering comprehensive health care services to their members for a fixed periodic payment. In such plans, the HMO is both insurer and provider in the sense of being obligated to furnish needed care as specified in the subscriber's contract.

National growth in HMO membership quintupled in just over a decade, increasing from 6 million people in 1976 to nearly 30 million members enrolled in a total of 556 HMOs in 1990, according to a 1991 InterStudy report.

Self-insurance also plays an important role in the private coverage system. In this arrangement, employers, not insurers, assume the risk, although insurers or third-party administrators (TPAs) may administer the plan.

Plans administered by employers, labor unions, fraternal societies, communities, and by rural and consumer health cooperatives often make health insurance available to specific groups of people who are not covered under conventional plans.

In 1989, 54 percent of insurance company group coverage was represented by ASO arrangements and minimum premium plans (MPPs). Under ASO arrangements, corporations and other organizations establish self-funded health plans and pay insurance carriers or private organizations a fee to process claims. Under MPPs, employers self-fund their plans yet insure against very large claims.

More than 77 million persons were covered in 1989 by self-insured plans, self-administered plans, and plans employing TPAs and HMOs.

◆ Types of Private Health Insurance

There is an endless variety of policies available in today's health insurance market, all containing a single coverage or combination of coverages available in the following major types of health insurance.

Hospital/Medical Insurance

Hospital expense coverage provides specific benefits for daily hospital room and board and usual hospital services and supplies during hospital confinements.

Room and board benefits are usually stated in one of two ways. Indemnity plans reimburse for the actual room-and-board charge up to a specified maximum dollar amount per day for hospital confinement. The second type provides a service-type benefit that pays the full cost of semiprivate room-and-board charge.

Hospital/medical coverage may be extended in one of three ways: a health insurance policy usually sold in combination with a physician's or surgical expense policy that provides benefits for both surgical operations and doctor's inhospital visits; a major medical policy that provides broad and substantial coverage for many types of medical expenses; or a combination of hospital-physician-surgical coverage plus a supplemental major medical policy.

Major Medical Expense Insurance

Major medical expense insurance, introduced nationally by insurance companies in 1951, has grown rapidly. There are two types of major medical plans. One supplements basic hospital-physician-surgeon expense insurance programs and the other offers comprehensive protection where both basic coverage and extended health care benefits are integrated. Major medical coverage offers broad and substantial protection for large, unpredictable medical expenses. It covers a wide range of medical charges with few internal limits and a high overall maximum benefit.

The majority of major medical policies whether written for individuals or under group plans are subject to some form of deductible and coinsurance payments by the insured person.

Medicare Supplement Policy

Medicare supplemental insurance, often referred to as a "Medigap" or "MedSup" policy, is accident and sickness insurance designed primarily as a supplement for hospital, medical, or surgical expenses for persons covered by Medicare.

Disability Income Protection (Loss of Income)

Disability income coverage replaces part of income lost by an employee as the result of an accident, illness, or pregnancy. Generally, disability income policies are divided into those that provide benefits for up to two years (short-term) and those that provide benefits for a longer period, usually for at least five years, to age 65, or for a lifetime (long-term).

When provided on a group basis, the benefits are usually integrated with benefits from Social Security and other public programs. The total benefits from these sources generally is set at a level that does not exceed 60 percent of earnings.

Individual disability income policies usually pay a fixed dollar amount of coverage. This amount may be greater for those who are turned down by Social Security. Individual disability income policies take many forms and may be designed to fit the special needs of the individual policy owner.

Dental Expense Insurance

Dental expense insurance, generally available through insurance company group plans, prepayment plans, and dental service corporations, reimburses for expenses of dental service and supplies and encourages preventive care. The coverage normally provides for oral examinations (including X-rays and cleaning), fillings, extractions, inlays, bridgework, and dentures, as well as oral surgery, root canal therapy, and orthodontics.

Plans normally include substantial consumer copayments, although the copayments may be lower for preventive services.

Long-Term Care Insurance

The market for insurance coverage that continues broad-ranged maintenance and health services to the chronically ill, disabled, or retarded began in earnest in 1985 when the number of companies selling this coverage doubled. The services provided by these policies may be provided on an inpatient or outpatient basis or entirely at home.

By December 1990, more than 1.9 million people had purchased long-term care insurance protection from more than 140 insurers.

Group Self-Insurance

The continuing growth in the number of insurance plans wherein the employer or union assumes all or part of the responsibility for paying claims made the nation's employers a principal bearer of the financial risks of illness and non-job-related injury in 1990.

There are two basic types of self-insured plans: fully insured and MPPs. In a totally self-insured plan, the employer assumes all the risk for paying claims. Under an MPP, the employer pays up to a specified maximum; then an insurer pays, or shares in the payment of additional claims. The administration of a self-insured plan includes claims processing, actuarial estimation of plan costs, and utilization review. The responsibilities may be assumed by the employer, an insurance carrier, a TPA, or a combination of all three.

These plans, as with fully insured plans, typically cover medical expenses under basic coverage only, major medical coverage only, or basic plus major medical coverage. Commercial insurance and Blue Cross-Blue Shield plans offer basic plus major medical coverage.

Most self-insured plans are freestanding major medical plans and do not contain a basic hospital benefit that provides full and unlimited coverage for hospital-related charges. In most self-insured plans, covered services are subject to a deductible and coinsurance.

◆ Employers Offering Health Insurance

Data from a 1990 survey of 3,192 firms show that most employees (81 percent) are offered health insurance, but only a minority of firms (42 percent) offer health coverage. The difference is explained by the large number of small firms that do not offer coverage. In general, the larger the firm, the more likely it is to offer coverage. (Table 2.4)

Coverage differs from industry to industry. Virtually all state and local government agencies offer health insurance. Goods-producing firms are more likely to offer health benefits than are service-producing firms.

Coverage less commonly is offered by firms employing significant proportions of low-wage workers, that have a large proportion of part-time workers, or that experience high employee turnover.

◆ The Population without Health Care Coverage

In recent years, the number of uninsured in this country has decreased slightly according to the Current Population Survey of the Bureau of the Census, from 31.5 million in 1988 to 31.3 million in 1989. Other sources place the figure in the range of 33 million to 35 million persons.

The Population without Health Care Coverage (1989) (Millions)				
	Total population	Number insured	Number without coverage	Percent without coverage
Total population	244.9	213.6	31.3	12.8
Under age 65 population	215.5	184.5	31.0	14.4

SOURCE: U. S. Department of Commerce, Bureau of the Census, Current Population Reports Series P-70, No.17.

The population without health insurance defies stereotype. Contrary to intuition, those who are uninsured are not predominately unemployed. Two-thirds of the uninsured population are in families of full-year steadily employed workers, most of whom were employed full-time. Nearly one-half of uninsured workers are self-employed or employed in firms with fewer than 25 workers. (Employee Benefit Research Institute, *Americans without Health Insurance*, July 1990.)

Several factors are responsible for growth in the uninsured population, including the economic downturn in the early 1980s and its effect on employment; erosion of the Medicaid program's coverage of the poor; demographic shifts; to a small extent, shifts of workers to industries less likely to offer health insurance; and finally, increased health care insurance costs that have outpaced growth in incomes.

Recent studies indicate that uninsured persons span all income groups but are predominantly in low- and middle-income families. The July 1990 survey by Employee Benefit Research Institute (EBRI) indicated that of the nonelderly population, 22.2 percent of the uninsured had incomes of $30,000 or more, 16.5 percent had incomes of $20,000 to $30,000, and the remaining people without health insurance earned salaries from under $10,000 up to $20,000. The federal poverty standard for a family of four in 1989 was $12,091. Fifteen percent of American children under age 18 are uninsured (9.2 million) and two-thirds of these uninsured children are older than 6 years.

In 1990, an HIAA survey of employers found cost to be the most important reason employers gave for not offering coverage. Other important reasons indicated were insufficient profits and no employee interest to provide health insurance coverage.

A Continuing Problem

Large numbers of uninsured people pose a major national problem for a variety of reasons. There is growing evidence that uninsured persons have difficulty gaining access to the health care system and if and when they do, it is often too late or more costly to treat the health problem. The cost of this care is borne indirectly by providers and insurers through the cost of "unsponsored care" or cost shifting. It has been estimated that the uninsured population is responsible for as much as 70 percent of unsponsored care.

◆ Health Insurance Claims

In 1989, private health insurers in the United States paid a total of $185.3 billion for medical care and disability claims (Table 2.6), an 8 percent increase over 1988. Commercial insurance companies paid more than one-half ($89.4 billion) of the total. This represents almost an 8 percent increase over the $83 billion paid in 1988.

Blue Cross-Blue Shield plans paid almost $51 billion in benefits in 1989. Self-insured and HMO plans paid almost $80 billion in paid claims for the same period.

Under hospital, surgical, physician expense, and major medical insurance, totaling almost $69 billion under group policies and $5 billion under individual policies in 1989, commercial insurers paid out an overall increase of 8 percent since 1988. (Tables 2.7 and 2.9) Dental claim payments totaled almost $7 billion in 1989.

Medicare supplement coverage disbursed more than $2 billion to claimants. Loss of income claims, including both short-term and long-term disability, in the amount of $7 billion were paid by insurance companies in 1989.

Many group insurance buyers began to turn to ASO and MPP instead of traditional insurance plans in the late 1970s and by 1989, 58 percent of the total group claims payments of the $82.2 billion paid by insurance companies came from these plans.

An HIAA survey of the 20 leading writers of health insurance conducted in July 1990 indicated an underwriting loss of 1.32 percent for group insurance, a continuation of the downward trend that began in 1986. (HIAA, *Operating Results from the Leading Writers of Group and Individual Health Insurance*, April 1991) Individual health insurance showed an even more alarming 8.85 percent underwriting loss.

The survey represents companies that write approximately 65 percent of the total group health insurance premiums and approximately 43 percent of the total individual health insurance premiums written by commercial insurance companies in the United States.

The dollar totals noted in this chapter refer to incurred claims. Premium figures reported are on an earned basis for the calendar year to reflect a true picture of premiums for the year.

Additions to claim reserves for persons already disabled are extracted from current year premiums but not reflected in the claims payments.

These claim reserves will be used to make future disability income payments under the contracts.

◆Health Insurance Premiums

In 1989, health insurance premium income for private insurance companies, self-insured and HMO plans, and Blue Cross-Blue Shield was $215.6 billion. Private insurance companies earned $108 billion in premiums in 1989; 85 percent of these premium dollars were for group insurance coverage. (Tables 2.1 and 2.12) Americans spent nearly 6 percent of disposable personal income (personal income minus personal taxes) in 1989 for health insurance premiums, the same as in 1988.

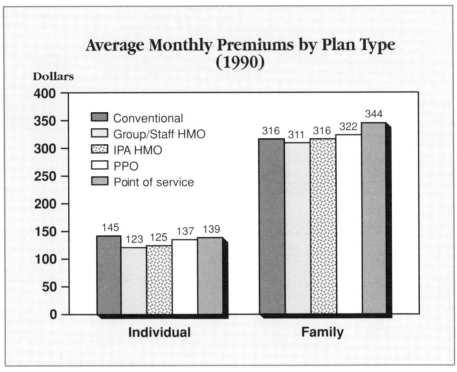

SOURCE: Health Insurance Association of America.

Group and Individual Premiums

Group health insurance premiums have been increasing mostly because of increasing health care costs.

In 1989, insurance companies earned $96 billion in group premiums and $12 billion in individual and family policy premiums. During this year, 54 percent of the group premiums were derived from self-insured arrangements. (For this analysis, premiums for self-insured plans [ASO and MPP] are defined as the sum of claims paid plus the insurer's administrative fee. (Table 2.12)

A recent HIAA survey of 3,192 large, mid-sized, and small employers from the public and private sectors found that in 1990 the average monthly premium for coverage in a conventional plan was $145 for an individual and $316 for a family.

For group or staff HMO coverage, it was $123 for an individual and $311 for a family. For PPOs, the monthly premium was $137 for an individual and $322 for a family; for the relatively new point-of-service plans, the monthly cost was $139 for an individual and $344 for a family. Average premium levels may not

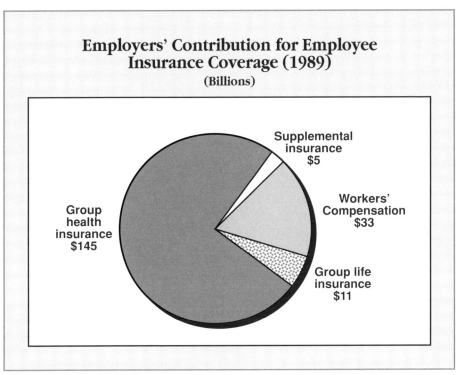

Employers' Contribution for Employee Insurance Coverage (1989)
(Billions)

Supplemental insurance $5

Workers' Compensation $33

Group health insurance $145

Group life insurance $11

SOURCE: U.S. Department of Commerce.

be good indicators of the relative efficiency of different plan types. The scope and level of benefits and the extent of patient cost sharing may differ from one plan type to another thus affecting premium levels.

PPOs and fee-for-service plans with preadmission certification continued to increase their market share during 1990.

According to the HIAA employers' survey, nearly 20 percent of individuals covered by employer-sponsored health insurance are members of an HMO; the combination of 13 percent in PPOs and 5 percent in point-of-service plans represents a total PPO market share of 17 percent, a 2 percent increase over 1989.

HIAA's *Health Insurance Picture 1990* reported that the majority of employers interviewed were satisfied with all aspects of their health plans for their employees. More than 90 percent planned to continue with their current health plans in 1991.

Insurance Premiums Paid by Employers

Between 1970 and 1980, the amount of insurance premiums paid by American employers for their employee group insurance policies increased by 352 percent. During the mid-1980s, premium increases were between 6 percent and 8 percent annually, but by 1989 premium increases were in double digits again. The pie chart on the preceding page shows that in 1989, employers contributed $145 billion for group health insurance to benefit their employees.

◆ The Evolution of Managed Care

During the past 5 to 10 years, the health care delivery and financing system has evolved at a pace that few expected, largely in response to the acute concern about the ever-rising cost of care. The most visible change has been the explosion of what are becoming known as managed care delivery systems, of which HMOs and PPOs are the best known examples.

A Definition of Managed Care

Although managed care is still evolving in response to changes in medical practice and the needs of consumers and payers, it can be defined as a system that integrates the financing and delivery of appropriate health care services to covered individuals and has the following common elements:

- Arrangements with selected providers to furnish a comprehensive set of health care services to members;
- Explicit standards for the selection of health care providers;
- Formal programs for ongoing quality assurance and utilization review; and
- Significant financial incentives for members to use providers and procedures covered by the plan.

Managed care plans employ a variety of techniques to assure quality and appropriateness of care including utilization review, case management, and the use of primary care physicians as coordinators and managers of care.

A variety of managed care models are in place and others will develop as the concept evolves.

History of Managed Care

Managed care began in the 1930s when the first prepaid group practices were established. The founders of this early type of managed care saw this model for integrating the financing and delivery of care as a way to improve quality and continuity of care and as a vehicle to provide preventive health care services.

Health maintenance organizations (HMOs).   The early prepaid group practices are one example of what are now known as HMOs. Since the 1930s, the HMO delivery system has evolved into a variety of forms. The characteristic they share is that they provide a defined, comprehensive set of health services to a voluntarily enrolled population within a specified geographic service area. Providers are typically reimbursed on a capitated or other "at risk" arrangement. There are a number of models. The group model, of which Kaiser Permanente is perhaps the best-known example, involves a physician medical group contracting with the entity that is financially responsible for covering enrollees. In the staff model, physicians are employees of the HMO.

In the network model, the HMO contracts with two or more independent group practices. The IPA-HMO contracts with a number of individual physicians in independent practices or with associations of independent physicians; IPA physicians often have arrangements with more than one HMO. The most recent model is the point-of-service plan, sometimes known as an HMO/PPO hybrid or an open-ended HMO. This model gives enrollees the option to choose providers outside the plan at the time they seek care for a particular condition, but there is a strong financial incentive to use the affiliated providers.

Although there was some growth in HMOs from the 1930s through the 1960s, particularly on the West Coast, interest in this alternative delivery system was sparked by the unanticipated rapid increases in health care costs that the country experienced in the late 1960s and 1970s. HMOs seemed to solve the cost problem by managing care to economize on services, particularly by reducing hospitalization rates.

In 1973, Congress enacted legislation to promote HMO growth. The HMO Act, P.L. 93-222, authorized federal funds to establish and develop HMOs over a period of five years. The act required most employers to offer an HMO option to employees where federally qualified HMOs were available. To meet the qualification tests, HMOs had to provide a prescribed range of basic health services and to offer the subscriber the opportunity to purchase optional health services.

In response to the favorable cost record of HMOs, Medicare and Medicaid also turned to HMOs with the hope that they could help bring the costs of these federal programs under control. Medicare participants in HMOs now number about 1 million. Medicaid increased its HMO enrollment from 282,000 in 1981 to 947,000 in 1987.

Overall, HMO growth has remained steady; enrollment increased from less than 2 million in the early 1970s to almost 34 million by June 1990, according to The InterStudy Edge, 1990. (Table 2.15) The Group Health Association

HMO Industry Profile, 1991, reported that more than 14 percent of all Americans were enrolled in 552 HMOs by the end of 1990. (Table 2.16)

Preferred provider organizations (PPOs). The other prominent example of managed care is the PPO. Developed during the 1980s, the PPO offers more flexibility than the HMO, giving consumers greater freedom in choosing providers, but, as with the HMO, it tries to achieve savings by directing patients to providers who are committed to cost-effective delivery of care.

PPOs are financing and delivery systems that combine features of standard fee-for-service indemnity plans and HMOs. Typically organized by insurers but sometimes by providers or others, PPOs have contracts with networks or panels of providers who agree to provide medical services and to be paid according to a negotiated fee schedule. Individuals who are enrolled in the PPO typically experience a financial penalty if they choose to get care from a non-affiliated provider, but that option is available. Ideally, providers are chosen for their efficiency, and the system monitors and controls to assure that care is efficiently provided.

The exclusive provider organization (EPO) is the extreme of the PPO. Services rendered by nonaffiliated providers are not reimbursed, so people belonging to an EPO must receive their care from affiliated providers or pay the entire cost out-of-pocket. Providers typically are reimbursed on a fee-for-service basis according to a negotiated discount or fee schedule.

Point-of-service plans (POS), sometimes called HMO-PPO hybrids or open-ended HMOs, combine characteristics of both HMOs and PPOs. POS plans utilize a network of selected contracted, participating providers. Employees select a primary care physician, who controls referrals for medical specialists. If an employee receives care from a plan provider, the employee pays little or nothing out-of-pocket as in an HMO and does not file claims. Care provided by out-of-plan providers will be reimbursed but employees must pay significantly higher copayments and deductibles. Providers may be reimbursed on a capitated basis or on a fee-for-service basis, however, there are usually financial incentives for providers to avoid overutilization.

The distinctions among HMOs, PPOs, and EPOs are becoming blurred. The Group Health Association of America reports that in 1988, among plans more than three years old, 47 percent added PPOs, indemnity options, open-ended options, freestanding utilization review services, or employee assistance programs to assist individuals with substance abuse or mental health problems. A small proportion also offered Workers' Compensation services. An increasing number of HMOs are offering a point-of-service option.

As cost-containment pressures continue and as these alternative delivery systems try to increase their market share, each tries to make its system more attractive. Often that means borrowing features from others. It is likely that the evolution will continue so that it will become increasingly difficult to characterize a particular managed care delivery system as adhering to any particular model.

Current Trends

HMO growth, which had been very rapid in recent years, slowed in 1990. The number of HMOs dropped from 556 in June 1990 to 552 by the end of the year. Sustaining the rapid growth rate of the previous five years would have been difficult.

HMOs currently enroll more than 14 percent of the population, with six states having more than 20 percent of their populations in HMOs. (Table 2.15) California, with more than 30 percent, has the highest HMO enrollment in both relative and absolute terms.

Alaska, Mississippi, and Wyoming were the only states that did not have operating HMOs in 1990. (Table 2.15)

Large HMOs (more than 100,000 members) grew at a rapid pace by the end of 1990. Although there are now 84 HMOs in the United States each with more than 100,000 members, 85 percent of all HMOs have fewer than 100,000 enrollees.

PPOs, primarily a phenomenon of the 1980s, also are growing rapidly. Survey results from the American College of Surgeons indicate an increase in number from 685 in 1989 to 798 in 1990 and at the end of 1990, 48 million people had access to a PPO according to the American Managed Care and Review Association. (Table 2.18)

The Directory of Preferred Provider Organizations of the American Association of Preferred Provider Organizations (AAPPO) shows a total of 824 PPOs covering over 38 million employees in 1990.

Differences in the number of PPOs and employees covered result from varying definitions of this type of organization in several surveys conducted during the past year.

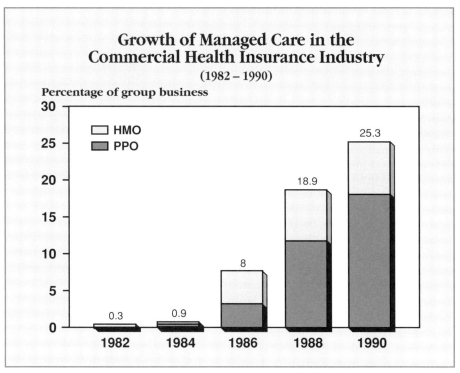

Growth of Managed Care in the Commercial Health Insurance Industry
(1982 – 1990)

Percentage of group business

SOURCE: HIAA Managed Care Survey, 1990.

Outlook for the Future

The recent rapid growth of managed care plans reflects the recognition by major employers and insurers that ways must be found to reduce costs while assuring that patients get appropriate care. Insurers increasingly see that un-managed fee-for-service indemnity plans do not have mechanisms to contain costs. As a consequence, many insurers have made major commitments to develop and sustain comprehensive managed care systems.

Table 2.1

Health Care Coverage in the United States (1984–1989) (Millions)

Characteristics	1984	1985	1986	1987	1988	1989
Total population	**233.5**	**235.5**	**238.2**	**240.4**	**243.1**	**244.9**
People with health care coverage, public and private						
Total	202.1	204.2	204.4	208.2	211.6	213.6
Percent of total population	86.6	86.7	85.8	86.6	87.1	87.2
Age of those covered						
0 to 64 years	175.6	177.2	176.8	179.9	182.8	184.5
65 and more years	26.5	27.1	27.5	28.3	28.8	29.1
Race						
White	174.2	175.2	175.2	176.2	181.3	183.1
Black	22.1	23.0	23.1	23.2	23.7	23.5
Hispanic	10.1	10.4	12.9	13.4	14.6	14.8
People with private insurance						
Total	177.4	180.1	180.1	183.2	188.4	189.0
Percent of total population	76.0	76.5	75.6	76.2	77.5	77.2
Age of those covered						
0 to 64 years	158.1	159.6	159.3	161.9	166.5	166.8
65 and more years	19.3	20.5	20.7	21.2	21.9	24.2
Race						
White	157.7	159.3	158.5	159.2	166.5	167.1
Black	15.3	15.9	16.3	16.9	16.5	17.0
Hispanic	7.6	7.8	9.8	9.9	11.4	11.8

NOTES: Hispanic may contain persons of any race. Totals may not add due to rounding or duplication. Data generated by pre-1990 Current Population Survey.
SOURCE: U.S. Department of Commerce, Bureau of the Census, Current Population Survey.

Table 2.2

People with Private Insurance Protection by Type of Insurer (Millions)

End of year	All insurers*	Insurance companies			Blue Cross-Blue Shield	Other plans**
		Total*	Group	Individual/family		
1940	12.0	3.7	2.5	1.2	6.0	2.3
1945	32.0	10.5	7.8	2.7	18.9	2.7
1950	76.6	37.0	22.3	17.3	38.8	4.4
1955	101.4	53.5	38.6	19.9	50.7	6.5
1960	122.5	69.2	54.4	22.2	58.1	6.0
1961	125.8	70.4	56.1	22.4	58.7	7.1
1962	129.4	72.2	58.1	23.1	60.1	6.9
1963	133.5	74.5	61.5	23.5	61.0	7.2
1964	136.3	75.8	63.1	34.0	62.1	6.8
1965	138.7	77.6	65.4	24.4	63.3	7.0
1966	142.4	80.4	67.8	24.9	65.3	6.6
1967	146.4	82.6	71.5	24.6	67.2	7.1
1968	151.9	85.7	74.1	25.3	70.1	7.3
1969	155.0	88.8	77.9	25.9	72.7	7.7
1970	158.8	89.7	80.5	26.7	75.1	8.1
1971	161.8	91.5	80.6	27.8	76.5	8.5
1972	164.1	93.7	81.5	29.1	78.2	8.1
1973	168.5	94.5	83.6	27.5	81.3	9.6
1974	173.1	97.0	85.4	28.8	83.8	11.1
1975	178.2	99.5	87.2	30.1	86.4	13.1
1976	176.9	97.0	86.8	27.0	86.6	14.9
1977	179.9	100.4	89.2	28.7	86.0	18.1
1978	185.7	106.0	92.6	36.1	85.8	21.5†
1979	185.7	104.1	94.1	34.4	86.1	25.5†
1980	187.4	105.5	97.4	33.8	86.7	33.2†
1981	186.2	105.9	103.0	25.3	85.8†	40.3†
1982	188.3	109.6	103.9	29.4	82.0†	48.2†
1983	186.6	105.9	104.6	22.2	79.6†	53.6†
1984	184.4	103.1	103.0	20.4	79.4†	54.4‡
1985	181.3	100.4	99.5	21.2	78.7†	55.1‡
1986	180.9	92.5	95.2***	11.7***	78.0†	64.9‡
1987	179.7	91.0	94.7***	10.0***	76.9†	66.9‡
1988	182.3	93.3	96.8***	10.7***	74.0†	71.3‡
1989	185.6	91.7	95.7*	9.7***	72.5†	77.1‡

*The data in these columns refer to the net total of persons protected by more than one kind of insuring organization or more than one insurance company policy providing the same type of coverage has been eliminated.

**Other plans include self-insured plans, self-administered plans, plans employing third-party administrators, and health maintenance organizations.

***Excludes hospital indemnity coverage, which had been included in prior years. For 1989, group hospital indemnity coverage was 6.3 million individuals and individual hospital indemnity was 8.9 million individuals.

†Estimate.

‡For 1984 and later, estimates of persons covered by "other plans" have been developed by HIAA in the absence of other available data.

NOTE: Some data were revised from previous editions. Data for 1978 and later have been adjusted downward due to new data on average family size. For 1975 and later, data include the number of persons covered in Puerto Rico and U.S. territories and possessions. Persons covered under insurance company ASO agreements and MPPs are included in the categories total Insurance companies and group policies.

NOTE: Data for 1987 and 1988 reflect the revised HIAA survey form and 1989 data reflect a change in the methodology.

SOURCES: Health Insurance Association of America, Blue Cross and Blue Shield Association, U.S. Department of Health and Human Services, Group Health Association of America, and Foster Higgins.

Table 2.3

Health Insurance Coverage by Age and Race (1986–1989)
(Percent)

Status	1986	1987	1988	1989
Total population	238,179,000	240,493,000	243,094,000	244,900,000
Private or government health insurance				
Total	85.9	86.8	87.0	87.1
Age:				
Less than 16 years	83.6	84.3	84.7	85.6
16 to 24 years	76.2	78.0	78.0	79.5
25 to 34 years	83.2	84.0	83.8	82.7
35 to 44 years	87.9	88.4	88.8	88.1
45 to 54 years	88.6	88.8	89.5	89.4
55 to 64 years	89.7	90.6	90.7	89.2
65 years and more	99.5	99.6	99.7	99.7
Race and Hispanic origin:				
White	87.1	87.8	88.3	87.8
Black	79.4	81.0	79.8	82.5
Hispanic	69.2	70.4	73.5	68.8
Covered by private health insurance				
Total	75.4	76.5	77.5	77.0
Age:				
Less than 16 years	69.2	69.7	71.2	71.9
16 to 24 years	68.9	70.9	71.4	72.3
25 to 34 years	75.8	77.0	77.6	75.9
35 to 44 years	82.3	82.6	83.2	82.4
45 to 54 years	82.8	83.6	84.6	83.6
55 to 64 years	82.1	83.3	83.6	80.9
65 years and more	75.8	77.9	79.0	78.4
Race and Hispanic origin:				
White	78.7	79.9	81.0	80.2
Black	54.9	56.1	55.3	58.4
Hispanic origin	50.8	53.9	57.4	53.3
Private health insurance (related to employment)				
Total	61.1	62.0	63.1	62.8
Age:				
Less than 16 years	59.7	60.8	61.9	61.5
16 to 24 years	53.9	54.6	55.7	56.5
25 to 34 years	67.7	69.1	70.1	69.0
35 to 44 years	74.5	74.4	75.2	75.3
45 to 54 years	72.4	73.3	74.7	74.9
55 to 64 years	66.5	66.9	68.0	64.8
65 years and more	33.3	34.3	35.0	35.5
Race and Hispanic origin:				
White	63.7	64.6	65.7	65.1
Black	45.4	46.2	46.8	49.8
Hispanic origin	43.5	45.9	48.6	45.9

Continued

Table 2.3 *(Continued)*

Status	1986	1987	1988	1989
Percent covered by Medicaid				
Total	7.2	7.3	7.1	7.4
Age:				
Less than 16 years	13.1	13.4	12.5	13.3
16 to 24 years	6.3	6.4	6.6	6.8
25 to 34 years	5.9	5.5	5.0	5.5
35 to 44 years	4.1	4.2	4.4	4.2
45 to 54 years	3.3	3.5	3.7	4.1
55 to 64 years	4.4	4.6	4.2	4.5
65 years and more	7.9	8.1	8.3	8.0
Race and Hispanic origin:				
White	5.2	5.1	4.9	4.9
Black	20.5	21.7	20.6	21.6
Hispanic	15.9	14.3	14.1	14.0

SOURCES: Health Insurance Coverage 1986–88 by Charles Nelson and Kathleen Short; Current Population Reports, Household Economic Studies, Survey of Income Participation, U.S. Department of Commerce, Bureau of the Census.

Table 2.4

Percent of Firms Offering Health Coverage by Associated Industry (1990)

	Percent of labor force	All firms	Number of employees		Percent of employees in firms offering coverage
			1 to 24 employees	25 or more employees	
Total	100	42	35	89	81
Agriculture	3	*	*	*	*
Mining	1	*	*	*	*
Construction	7	43	38	94	68
Manufacturing	19	55	46	93	89
Transportation**	7	44	*	100	80
Wholesale trade	4	44	38	87	78
Retail trade	17	32	27	84	68
Finance**	7	48	42	92	84
Business services	32	42	36	90	81
Government**	5	60	*	99	93

*Insufficient sample.
**Transportation includes communications and public utilities: Finance includes insurance and real estate; Government includes state and local entities only.
SOURCES: Health Insurance Association of America and Bureau of Labor Statistics, January 1990.

Table 2.5

Firms That Offer Health Benefits and Firms That Do Not Offer Health Benefits by Size (1990) (Percent)

Firm size	Offer health benefits	Do not offer health benefits
Total	**42**	**58**
Fewer than 10 employees	27	73
10 to 24 employees	73	27
25 to 99 employees	87	13
25 to 49 employees	85	15
50 to 99 employees	89	11
100 or more employees	98	2

NOTE: Total may not add to 100% because of rounding.
SOURCE: HIAA. Critical Distinctions: How Firms That Offer Health Benefits Differ from Those That Do Not.

Table 2.6

Private Health Insurance Claims Payments by Type of Insurer (Billions)

Year	Insurance companies	Blue Cross-Blue Shield	Self-insured & HMO plans	Total
1950	$ 0.8	$ 0.6	NA	$ 1.3
1955	1.8	1.4	NA	3.1
1960	3.0	2.6	NA	5.7
1965	5.2	4.5	NA	9.6
1970	9.1	8.1	NA	17.2
1975	16.5	16.9	NA	32.1
1980	37.0	25.5	$16.2	76.3
1981	41.6	29.2	18.9	85.9
1982	49.2	32.2	21.6	97.1
1983	51.7	34.4	24.1	104.1
1984	56.0	35.7	26.1	107.5
1985	60.0	37.5	32.5	117.6
1986	64.3	40.6	36.8	128.5
1987	72.5	44.5	56.5	151.7
1988	83.0	48.2	62.8	171.1
1989	89.4	50.7	79.8	185.3

SOURCE: Health Insurance Association of America, Annual Survey of Health Insurance Companies.

Table 2.7

Group Health Claims Payments of Insurance Companies by Type of Coverage (Billions)

Year	Total group	Hospital/ Medical	Dental	Medicare supplement	Loss of income
1950	$ 0.4	NA	NA	NA	NA
1955	1.3	NA	NA	NA	NA
1960	2.4	$ 1.8	NA	NA	$0.8
1965	4.0	3.3	NA	NA	1.0
1970	7.5	6.0	$0.1	NA	1.8
1975	14.2	11.6	0.6	NA	2.7
1980	33.0	25.8	2.8	$0.1	4.3
1981	37.7	30.0	3.5	0.2	4.2
1982	44.2	35.9	4.0	0.1	4.1
1983	46.9	38.6	4.4	0.1	3.9
1984	50.3	41.1	4.9	0.4	3.9
1985	53.7	43.9	5.3	0.5	4.0
1986	58.9	48.1	5.3	1.5	4.0
1987	66.5	54.6	5.9	1.5	4.6
1988	76.4	63.3	6.3	2.2	4.6
1989	82.2	68.6	6.5	2.1	5.0

SOURCE: Health Insurance Association of America, Annual Survey of Health Insurance Companies.

Table 2.8

Group Health Claims Payments of Insurance Companies by Type of Risk Management (Billions)

Year	Total group	Fully insured		Administrative services only		Minimum premium plan	
		Hospital/ Medical	Loss of income	Hospital/ Medical	Loss of income	Hospital/ Medical	Loss of income
1950	$ 0.4	NA	NA	NA	NA	NA	NA
1955	1.3	NA	NA	NA	NA	NA	NA
1960	2.4	$ 1.8	NA	NA	NA	NA	NA
1965	4.0	3.3	NA	NA	NA	NA	NA
1970	7.5	6.0	NA	NA	NA	NA	NA
1975	14.2	11.6	NA	NA	NA	NA	NA
1980	33.9	21.7	$3.8	$ 2.2	$0.2	$ 5.6	$0.4
1981	37.7	19.8	3.2	3.6	0.3	10.2	0.7
1982	44.2	21.7	3.0	5.4	0.4	13.0	0.8
1983	46.9	22.8	2.9	5.7	0.2	14.5	0.7
1984	50.3	20.6	2.7	9.7	0.4	16.1	0.8
1985	53.7	21.5	2.8	11.8	0.5	16.3	0.8
1986	58.9	23.1	2.7	14.1	0.7	17.7	0.6
1987	66.5	27.8	3.0	17.8	0.9	16.4	0.7
1988	76.4	32.5	3.1	22.0	0.9	17.4	0.5
1989	82.2	31.3	3.5	28.3	1.0	17.7	0.4

SOURCE: Health Insurance Association of America, Annual Survey of Insurance Companies.

Table 2.9

Individual Health Insurance Claims Payments of Insurance Companies by Type of Coverage (Billions)

Year	Total individual	Hospital/ Medical	Loss of income
1978	$3.5	$2.5	$1.0
1979	3.8	2.6	1.1
1980	4.0	3.0	1.0
1981	3.9	3.0	1.0
1982	4.5	3.6	1.4
1983	4.8	3.8	1.0
1984	5.7	4.4	1.3
1985	6.3	4.7	1.6
1986	5.4	3.8	1.6
1987	5.9	4.1	1.8
1988	6.6	4.7	1.8
1989	7.2	5.0	2.2

SOURCE: Health Insurance Association of America, Annual Survey of Insurance Companies.

Table 2.10

Health Insurance Premiums of Insurance Companies, Self-Insured, HMOs, and Blue Cross-Blue Shield (Billions)

Year	Private insurance Net total premiums	All types*	Self-insured and HMO plans	Blue Cross-Blue Shield
1950	$ 2.0	$ 1.3	NA	$ 0.7
1955	4.3	2.7	NA	1.5
1960	7.5	4.7	NA	2.8
1965	12.1	7.4	NA	4.8
1970	20.0	11.5	NA	8.4
1975	37.0	20.8	NA	17.6
1980	84.7	43.7	$17.3	26.3
1981	95.1	49.0	20.0	30.4
1982	109.5	58.3	22.9	34.3
1983	119.9	63.2	25.6	37.6
1984	127.6	70.4	28.6	40.0
1985	139.5	75.2	36.7	41.5
1986	143.4	75.5	40.6	43.5
1987	167.1†	84.1	59.8‡	46.3
1988	189.9†	98.2	71.1‡	51.2
1989	215.6†	108.0	89.1‡	56.0

*Does not add to sum of types because of duplication among types.
†Estimate.
‡For 1984 and later, estimates of persons covered by "other plans."
NOTE: Insurance company premiums reported in Tables 2.10 through 2.13 are on an earned basis for the calendar year. Earned premiums are defined as the calendar-year portion of premiums for which the protection of the policy has been provided.
SOURCE: Health Insurance Association of America, Annual Survey of Insurance Companies.

Table 2.11

Group Health Insurance Premiums of Insurance Companies by Type of Coverage (Billions)

Year	Total group	Hospital/ Medical	Dental	Medicare supplement	Loss of income
1980	36.8	28.2	3.2	0.0	5.3
1981	42.5	33.0	4.1	0.1	5.2
1982	50.0	39.6	4.8	0.1	5.5
1983	54.9	44.4	5.3	0.1	5.1
1984	60.8	49.6	5.7	0.5	5.0
1985	64.4	52.7	6.2	0.6	4.8
1986	65.9	53.0	6.2	1.8	5.0
1987	74.0	59.9	6.8	1.8	5.5
1988	87.6	71.9	7.8	2.5	5.5
1989	96.1	79.3	7.8	3.0	6.0

SOURCE: Health Insurance Association of America, Survey of Health Insurance Companies.

Table 2.12

Group Health Insurance Premiums of Insurance Companies by Type of Risk Management (Billions)

Year	Total group premiums	Fully insured Hospital/ Medical	Loss of income	Administrative service only Hospital/ Medical	Loss of income	Minimum premium plan Hospital/ Medical	Loss of income
1980	$36.8	$23.0	$4.6	$ 2.4	$0.2	$ 6.1	$0.5
1981	42.5	22.4	4.1	4.0	0.3	10.9	0.9
1982	50.0	24.6	4.2	5.7	0.4	14.2	0.9
1983	54.9	27.5	3.8	6.1	0.5	16.2	0.9
1984	60.8	26.9	3.5	10.7	0.5	18.2	1.0
1985	64.4	27.6	3.5	13.1	0.6	18.8	0.8
1986	65.9	27.1	3.4	15.4	0.8	18.4	0.8
1987	74.0	30.7	3.7	18.7	1.0	19.1	0.7
1988	87.6	36.9	3.8	25.2	1.1	20.0	0.6
1989	96.1	39.0	4.4	30.8	1.1	20.3	0.5

SOURCE: Health Insurance Association of America, Survey of Health Insurance Companies.

Table 2.13

Individual Health Insurance Premiums of Insurance Companies by Type of Coverage (Billions)

Year	Total individual	Hospital/ Medical	Loss of income
1980	$ 6.9	$4.9	$2.0
1981	6.5	4.7	1.8
1982	8.3	5.8	2.5
1983	8.3	6.3	2.0
1984	9.6	7.2	2.4
1985	10.8	7.9	2.9
1986	9.6	6.7	2.9
1987	10.1	7.0	3.1
1988	10.6	7.4	3.2
1989	11.8	8.2	3.6

SOURCE: Health Insurance Association of America, Survey of Health Insurance Companies.

Table 2.14

Underwriting Results from the 20 Largest Writers of Group and Individual Health Insurance in the United States (1984–1989)

Year	Net underwriting loss or gain (Thousands)	Net underwriting loss or gain (Percent)
Group health insurance		
1984	$ 454,501	2.38
1985	57,459	0.31
1986	(378,848)	(2.05)
1987	(816,195)	(3.92)
1988	(1,097,838)	(4.62)
1989	345,828	(1.32)
Individual health insurance		
1984	($ 61,195)	(1.53)
1985	(46,875)	(1.14)
1986	(125,355)	(2.88)
1987	(295,901)	(6.20)
1988	(399,930)	(8.43)
1989	(469,297)	(8.85)

NOTE: Parentheses denote negative figure or percentage.
SOURCE: Health Insurance Association of America.

Table 2.15

HMO Enrollment and Percent of Population in HMOs by State (1990)

Number of HMOs	State	Enrollment	Percent of population in HMOs
556	Total	33,621,475	13.5
5	Alabama	217,179	5.3
0	Alaska	0	0.0
13	Arizona	574,918	16.2
3	Arkansas	52,692	2.2
46	California	8,920,713	30.7
18	Colorado	664,663	20.0
12	Connecticut	643,359	19.9
6	Delaware	117,448	17.5
4	District of Columbia	486,039	72.9
29	Florida	1,338,106	10.6
8	Georgia	308,379	4.8
3	Guam	59,814	44.7
5	Hawaii	240,477	21.6
1	Idaho	17,804	1.8
26	Illinois	1,469,838	12.6
12	Indiana	339,026	6.1
7	Iowa	286,278	10.1
8	Kansas	199,351	7.9
7	Kentucky	210,989	5.7
9	Louisiana	237,346	5.4
3	Maine	32,048	2.6
11	Maryland	666,828	14.2
19	Massachusetts	1,567,051	26.5
17	Michigan	1,407,998	15.2
11	Minnesota	712,373	15.2
0	Mississippi	0	0.0
17	Missouri	541,750	10.5
1	Montana	5,200	1.0
5	Nebraska	82,266	5.1
3	Nevada	94,555	8.5
2	New Hampshire	106,242	9.6
15	New Jersey	955,075	12.3
5	New Mexico	194,665	12.7
37	New York	2,709,925	15.1
12	North Carolina	315,111	4.8
2	North Dakota	11,010	1.7
34	Ohio	1,454,020	13.3
6	Oklahoma	176,159	5.5
9	Oregon	696,709	24.7
20	Pennsylvania	1,384,743	11.5
4	Rhode Island	205,859	20.6
4	South Carolina	67,105	1.9
1	South Dakota	23,683	3.3
9	Tennessee	183,601	3.7
26	Texas	1,167,925	6.9
5	Utah	237,621	13.9
1	Vermont	36,570	6.4
13	Virginia	374,491	6.1
8	Washington	696,590	14.6
1	West Virginia	72,295	3.9
28	Wisconsin	1,057,588	21.7
0	Wyoming	0	0.0

SOURCE: InterStudy, The InterStudy Edge 1991, Vol. 5.

Table 2.16

Number of HMOs and HMO Enrollment by Selected Characteristics (1989–1990)

Selected characteristics	Plans		Enrollment	
	Number of plans	Percent of total	Number of enrollees	Percent of total
All plans	552	100.0	34,556,700	100.0
Model type				
Staff	60	10.8	4,381,373	12.7
Group	77	13.9	10,365,008	29.9
Network	82	14.9	5,071,842	14.7
IPA	333	60.4	14,738,477	42.7
Region				
New England	39	7.2	2,552,788	7.4
Mid-Atlantic	68	12.3	4,763,921	13.8
Midwest	170	30.7	8,296,128	24.0
South Atlantic	90	16.3	3,806,271	11.0
South Central	69	12.5	2,548,788	7.4
Mountain	41	7.4	2,124,892	6.1
Pacific	75	13.6	10,464,412	30.3
Plan size				
0–19,999 individuals	213	38.6	2,135,756	6.2
20,000–49,999 individuals	171	31.0	5,376,171	15.6
50,000–99,999 individuals	79	14.3	5,653,675	16.4
100,000 or more individuals	68	12.3	9,578,641	27.6
250,000 or more individuals	21	3.8	11,812,457	34.2
Plan age				
2–3 years	89	16.1	1,299,306	3.8
4–7 years	272	49.6	9,188,324	26.6
8–15 years	125	22.6	11,642,761	33.7
16–25 years	49	8.9	4,729,897	13.7
26+	17	3.1	7,696,415	22.3
Tax status				
Nonprofit	274	49.6	18,654,438	54.0
Profit-making	278	50.4	15,902,262	46.0
Qualification status				
Federally qualified	304	55.4	26,366,682	76.3
Nonqualified	248	44.9	8,190,018	23.7

SOURCE: Group Health Association, HMO Industry Profile, 1991.

Table 2.17

Percent of Health Plans Providing Coverage for Specific Services by Plan Type (1989–1990)

Benefits	Conventional insurance plan		PPO plan		HMO IPA plan		HMO staff plan		Point-of-service plan	
	1989	1990	1989	1990	1989	1990	1989	1990	1989	1990
Adult physical exams	34	30	42	49	95	94	99	97	NA	87
Mammographies	NA	57	NA	70	NA	95	NA	96	NA	92
Pap smears	NA	55	NA	70	NA	97	NA	99	NA	93
Childhood immunizations	NA	47	NA	65	NA	97	NA	99	NA	90
Well-child care	NA	39	NA	58	NA	96	NA	97	NA	98
Well-baby care	50	48	NA	68	98	98	99	98	NA	93
Preventive diagnostic procedures	67	NA	NA	NA	94	NA	100	NA	NA	NA
Prescription drugs	NA	NA	NA	NA	NA	NA	NA	NA	NA	NA
Home health care	73	NA	75	89	90	89	88	86	NA	88
Mental health										
Outpatient	90	93	91	93	98	97	99	93	NA	92
Inpatient	95	96	95	96	99	96	97	95	NA	92
Substance abuse treatment	NA	NA	NA	NA	NA	NA	NA	NA	NA	NA
Alcohol	85	93	88	94	95	95	98	96	NA	97
Drugs	86	93	87	94	96	94	98	95	NA	96
General dental care	37	39	39	37	17	24	11	21	NA	32
Orthodontia	NA	NA	NA	NA	NA	NA	NA	NA	NA	NA
Hospice care	NA	82	NA	NA	NA	80	NA	72	NA	82
Chiropractic care	NA	85	NA	78	NA	54	NA	42	NA	72
Eye care	NA	24	NA	28	NA	52	NA	62	NA	40
In vitro fertilization	NA	23	NA	19	NA	24	NA	29	NA	32

SOURCE: HIAA Employer Survey, 1990.

Table 2.18

Operational PPOs (1987–1990)

Years	1987	1988	1989	1990
Total United States	**572**	**618**	**685**	**798**
Alabama	8	6	7	10
Alaska	2	0	0	1
Arizona	27	22	13	24
Arkansas	4	2	1	5
California	98	104	152	112
Colorado	29	31	24	35
Connecticut	4	4	90	8
Delaware	1	0	0	0
District of Columbia	9	6	3	5
Florida	37	40	25	55
Georgia	17	17	16	0
Hawaii	2	2	2	2
Idaho	0	0	0	0
Illinois	32	32	34	31
Indiana	10	9	7	14
Iowa	3	3	3	3
Kansas	7	10	6	13
Kentucky	9	8	8	5
Louisiana	12	11	13	11
Maine	0	0	0	0
Maryland	12	9	15	23
Massachusetts	11	13	37	21
Michigan	17	17	8	34
Minnesota	14	11	7	11
Mississippi	2	1	3	4
Missouri	22	20	11	27
Montana	0	0	0	0
Nebraska	3	3	2	8
Nevada	9	6	6	8
New Hampshire	1	0	1	0
New Jersey	4	2	5	8
New Mexico	7	2	2	5
New York	8	10	7	17
North Carolina	11	10	9	15
North Dakota	1	1	0	0
Ohio	44	53	35	62
Oklahoma	11	8	7	10
Oregon	13	8	6	11
Pennsylvania	28	32	34	37
Rhode Island	0	0	0	1
South Carolina	4	4	1	4
South Dakota	0	1	0	0
Tennessee	21	20	13	22
Texas	21	30	39	55
Utah	7	5	4	8
Vermont	0	0	0	0
Virginia	8	10	7	15
Washington	21	20	17	19
West Virginia	3	4	2	4
Wisconsin	10	9	3	13
Wyoming	1	1	0	1
Puerto Rico	1	1	0	1

SOURCE: American College of Surgeons, 1990 Socio-Economic Factbook for Surgery.

Chapter 3

PUBLIC HEALTH CARE COVERAGE— EXPENDITURES AND ENROLLMENT

◆ Federal, State, and Local Health Care Programs

In 1990, all levels of government combined spent $283 billion to fund medical and health care services, research, and medical facility construction. The government share represented more than 42 percent of total national health expenditures.

Government health expenditures increased by 11 percent between 1989 and 1990, compared with 10.4 percent for total public and private expenditures. Per capita government expenditures were $1,089 for 1990.

National Health Expenditures in Billions (1985–1990)						
	1985	1986	1987	1988	1989	1990
Total	$423	$455	$494	$546	$603	$666
Private	248	265	286	319	350	384
Public	175	190	208	227	253	283
Federal	124	133	144	158	175	195
State/local	51	58	64	71	78	87

SOURCE: U.S. Department of Health and Human Services, Health Care Financing Administration.

◆ Federal Programs

The majority of federal health spending is for health services provided to six major groups: low-income individuals and others eligible for Medicaid, those over age 65 (Medicare), military personnel and their dependents, veterans, federal civilian employees, and native Americans.

Medicare

Medicare, effective since July 1, 1966, is a federally administered program that provides hospital and medical insurance protection to those persons age 65 and older, disabled persons under age 65 who receive cash benefits under Social Security or Railroad Retirement programs, and people of all ages with chronic kidney disease. Since 1973 aliens and some federal civil service employees and annuitants have been eligible to enroll by paying a monthly premium.

Many aged or disabled members who are covered by Medicare also are covered by Medicaid. Where this dual coverage exists, most state Medicaid programs pay the Medicare premiums, deductibles and copayments, and in some cases pay for services not covered by Medicare.

Medicare consists of compulsory hospitalization insurance (HI) called Part A and voluntary supplementary medical insurance (SMI) called Part B, which pays for physicians' services, medical services, and supplies not covered under Part A. Part A is financed by contributions from employers, employees, and participants; Part B is voluntary and is financed by monthly premiums paid by those who enroll and by the federal government.

On January 1, 1991, Medicare's Part A deductible rose from $592 to $628. The monthly Part B premium increased from $28.60 to $28.90. For 1991 the daily coinsurance amount is $157 for the 61st day of hospitalization through 90th day and $78.50 for the 21st through 100th days of extended care in a skilled nursing facility. The Part B deductible rose from $75 to $100. Blue Cross-Blue Shield plans and several other independent organizations serve as fiscal intermediaries for the government.

More than 6,300 hospitals have an agreement to participate under the Medicare prospective payment system (PPS). Exceptions are psychiatric, children's, long-term care, and rehabilitation hospitals, and medical facilities that have an approved waiver.

Enrollment in the Medicare program increased from 32.9 million in 1988 to 33.6 million in 1989. With an increase in this country's population and longer life expectancies, the Medicare program enrollment will continue to climb in the coming years.

In 1989, 14.6 million males and 19 million females were enrolled in the program. More than $94 billion was paid by the federal government on behalf of Medicare enrollees in 1989.

Projections by the Health Care Financing Administration (HCFA) indicate that by 2050 there will be 69 million people aged 65 years or over who will be eligible for Medicare. Of this number, 15 million will be age 85 or more.

Medicaid

This federal-state program of medical assistance helps certain low-income individuals and families. Administered by each state according to designated federal requirements and guidelines, the program is financed from both state and federal funds. It provides medical assistance to persons who are eligible for cash assistance programs such as Aid to Families of Dependent Children (AFDC) and Supplemental Security Income (SSI). Medicaid benefits also may be available to other persons who have enough income for basic living expenses but cannot afford to pay for their medical care.

To qualify for federal matching funds, the law requires state programs to include inpatient and outpatient hospital services, laboratory and X-ray services, and skilled nursing and home health services for individuals aged 21 and older. Services such as periodic screening, diagnosis and treatment, family planning for children under age 21, and physicians' services also must be provided. Participation in the Medicaid program is optional but currently all states participate.

Studies by a few research organizations have shown that higher provider fees create greater access to care for poor patients, but recent findings have shown that access to care is not hampered (with the possible exception of obstetrical care) by low Medicaid fees because Medicaid recipients in states with low fee scales wind up getting care in hospital outpatient departments and emergency rooms, health department clinics, and community and migrant health centers.

Medicaid Fees by Procedure (1989)

Procedure	Minimum	Median	Maximum
Comprehensive office visit, new patient	$ 10	$ 44	$ 104
Limited office visit, established patient	10	17	39
Intermediate office visit, established patient	10	20	46
Intermediate emergency visit	8	25	118
Comprehensive consultation, initial	20	60	146
Psychotherapy, 45 to 50 minutes	18	42	86
Comprehensive hospital visit, initial	10	51	150
Intermediate hospital visit, subsequent	6	20	70
Total obstetric care, vaginal delivery	344	738	1,316
Total obstetric care, Cesarean delivery	453	903	1,605
Tonsillectomy and adenoidectomy under 12 years of age	60	164	475
Repair inguinal hernia, under 5 years of age	140	312	1,016
Total hysterectomy	166	614	1,770
Cataract removal	404	990	2,915
Electrocardiogram	10	23	55
Chest X-ray, two views	10	23	55
Endoscopy, upper GI	80	225	411
EPSDT screening and diagnostic services	14	34	95

SOURCE: Physician Payment Review Commission, 1990.

As indicated in Table 3.2, the Medicaid program paid almost $65 billion for services given to more than 25 million recipients in 1990.

Utilization of Medicare and Medicaid Services

Fifty-nine million Americans received services paid for by Medicare or Medicaid in 1990, according to HCFA. One out of five beneficiaries (9 million) used inpatient hospital services, 44 million received reimbursable physician services, 35 million were paid for outpatient visits, and more than 932,000 received benefits for care in skilled nursing facilities. Medicaid provided 14.3 million people with prescription drugs and a combination of Medicare and Medicaid benefits provided services to 2.6 million recipients of home health care.

◆ Other Government Services

Military Personnel and Dependents

Treatment at any Department of Defense installation medical facility is available to all active and retired military personnel and their dependents. A program called the Civilian Health and Medical Program of the Uniformed Services (CHAMPUS) is designed for military families unable to use government medical facilities because of distance, overcrowding, or unavailability of appropriate medical treament.

After a deductible is met, CHAMPUS pays for medical care. Retired military personnel, their dependents, and dependents of deceased personnel are compensated by CHAMPUS if they are not eligible for Medicare. CHAMPUS accounted for $2.8 billion of the $13 billion budgeted by the Department of Defense in 1989.

Federal Civilian Employees

The Federal Employees Health Benefits Program (FEHBP) provides voluntary health insurance coverage for approximately 9 million federal government employees: 2.5 million active employees, 1.5 million annuitants, and 5 million dependents. Approximately 72 percent of all federal employees and annuitants were enrolled in FEHBP in 1990; the remaining 28 percent were either ineligible or had waived FEHBP coverage. The annual cost will be an estimated $14.5 billion in 1991.

FEHBP is characterized by a multiple choice among competing health plans: enrollees may choose among plans with varying levels of benefits and premiums during the annual open enrollment period.

The FEHBP offers three major types of plans: (1) government-wide plans which beginning in 1990 include only a service benefit plan administered by the National Blue Cross and Blue Shield Association; (2) employee organization plans which are sponsored by employee organizations or unions and are open only to employees or annuitants who become members of the sponsoring organization; and (3) comprehensive medical plans, or HMOs that offer health care by designated plan physicians, hospitals, and other providers in designated geographic locations. There are presently 350 HMOs in FEHBP, 25 of which offer two options.

The federal government and enrollees jointly finance the program through premium payments, with the government paying approximately 74 percent of the average of all plan premiums. The Office of Personnel Management (OPM) administers FEHBP.

In addition to federal payment of the employer contributions under these programs, the government also incurs administrative expenses for the operation of on-site health care facilities for federal civilian employees.

Veterans Medical Care

The government budgeted $234.7 million for Veterans Administration medical care and research in 1989. In addition, the Veterans Administration operates 162 medical centers for the care of individuals who served honorably in the armed forces. Patients with service-related ailments receive top priority.

Indian Health Services

More than $1.3 billion in federal funds was appropriated in 1990 to provide medical care and health services for more than 1 million native American Indian and Alaskan natives.

◆ State and Local Programs

The public health programs of state health agencies and local health departments can be divided into four primary program areas: personal health, environmental health, health resources, and laboratory services. In addition to these primary programs, the agencies also perform general administrative and service functions. Not all state health agencies perform the same services. In some states, designated expenditures for mental health care may be controlled by a separate mental health agency.

During fiscal year 1989 (the latest year for which data is available), 55 state health agencies spent a total of $11.8 billion for their public health programs. (Table 3.5)

State health agencies expenditures for 1989 were for maternal and child health, communicable diseases, handicapped children, dental health, chronic disease, mental health, state health agency-operated institutions, home health care, and services to special population groups (i.e., immigrants and refugees).

There were nearly 3,000 local health departments in 1989. Of all the U.S. territories and possessions (except Puerto Rico and American Samoa), three states and the District of Columbia do not have local health departments.

Table 3.1

Medicare Enrollment and Payments (1967–1989)

Year	Hospital and/or medical insurance Part A + B — Number of enrolled persons (millions)	Benefit payments (billions)	Hospital insurance Part A — Number of enrolled persons (millions)	Benefit payments (billions)	Supplementary medical insurance Part B — Number of enrolled persons (millions)	Benefit payments (billions)
All enrollees						
1967	19.5	$ 3.1	19.5	$ 2.5	17.9	$ 0.7
1968	19.8	5.1	19.8	3.7	18.8	1.4
1969	20.1	6.3	10.0	4.7	19.2	1.6
1970	20.5	6.8	20.4	4.8	19.6	1.9
1971	20.9	7.5	20.7	5.4	19.9	2.1
1972	21.3	8.4	21.1	6.1	20.4	2.3
1973	23.5	9.0	23.3	6.6	22.5	2.4
1974	24.2	10.7	23.9	7.8	23.2	2.9
1975	25.0	14.1	24.6	10.4	23.9	2.8
1976	25.7	16.9	25.3	12.2	24.6	4.7
1977	26.5	20.8	26.1	14.9	25.4	5.9
1978	27.1	24.3	26.8	17.4	26.1	6.9
1979	27.9	28.1	27.5	19.9	26.8	8.3
1980	28.5	33.9	28.1	23.8	27.4	10.1
1981	29.1	41.2	28.6	28.9	27.9	12.3
1982	29.5	49.2	29.1	34.3	28.4	14.8
1983	30.1	55.6	29.6	38.1	28.9	17.5
1984	30.5	60.9	30.0	41.5	29.4	19.5
1985	31.1	69.5	30.6	47.7	29.9	21.8
1986	31.8	74.1	31.2	48.9	30.6	25.2
1987	32.4	79.8	31.9	49.8	31.2	29.9
1988	32.9	85.5	32.4	51.9	31.6	33.7
1989	33.6	94.3	33.1	57.4	32.1	36.9
Age 65 and more						
1967	19.5	$ 3.2	19.5	$ 2.5	17.9	$ 0.7
1968	19.8	5.1	19.7	3.7	18.8	1.3
1969	20.1	6.3	20.1	4.7	19.2	1.6
1970	20.5	6.8	20.4	4.8	19.6	1.9
1971	20.9	7.4	20.7	5.4	19.9	2.1
1972	21.3	8.3	21.2	6.1	20.4	2.3
1973	21.8	9.0	21.6	6.6	20.9	2.4
1974	22.3	9.6	21.9	7.1	21.4	2.5
1975	22.8	12.7	22.5	9.4	21.9	3.3
1976	23.3	15.1	22.9	11.0	22.4	4.0
1977	23.8	18.3	23.5	13.3	22.9	5.0
1978	24.4	21.2	23.9	15.4	23.5	5.8
1979	24.9	24.4	24.6	17.5	24.1	6.9
1980	25.5	29.4	25.1	20.9	24.7	8.5
1981	26.1	35.9	25.6	25.5	25.2	10.4
1982	26.5	42.6	26.1	30.2	25.7	12.4
1983	27.1	48.4	26.7	33.6	26.3	14.8
1984	27.6	53.6	27.1	36.8	26.8	16.8
1985	28.2	61.5	27.7	42.4	27.3	19.1
1986	28.8	65.4	28.3	43.4	27.9	22.1
1987	29.4	70.7	28.8	44.4	28.3	26.4
1988	29.9	76.1	29.3	46.4	28.8	29.8
1989	30.4	88.3	29.9	53.5	29.2	34.8

NOTE: Detail may not add due to rounding.

SOURCE: U.S.Department of Health and Human Services, Health Care Financing Administration, Bureau of Data Management and Strategy.

Table 3.2

Medicaid Recipients and Benefits Paid by Federal and State Governments (1972–1990)

Fiscal year	Total		Age 65 and more		Dependent children under 21 and adults in family with dependent children		All others including blind recipients and disabled	
	Annual recipients (millions)	Annual benefits paid (billions)	Annual recipients (millions)	Annual benefits paid (billions)	Annual recipients (millions)	Annual benefits paid (billions)	Annual recipients (millions)	Annual benefits paid (billions)
1972	17.6	$ 6.3	3.3	$ 1.9	11.1	$ 2.1	3.3	$ 2.2
1973	19.6	8.7	3.5	3.2	12.7	2.9	3.3	2.5
1974	21.5	9.9	3.7	3.7	13.9	3.4	3.7	2.8
1975	22.0	12.2	3.6	4.4	14.1	4.2	4.2	3.6
1976	22.8	14.1	3.6	4.9	14.7	4.7	4.4	4.3
1977	22.8	16.2	3.6	5.5	14.4	5.2	4.6	5.3
1978	21.9	17.9	3.4	6.3	14.1	5.4	4.5	6.1
1979	21.5	20.5	3.4	7.1	13.7	5.9	4.4	7.3
1980	21.7	23.3	3.4	8.7	14.2	6.3	4.3	7.9
1981	21.9	27.2	3.4	9.9	14.8	7.3	4.7	9.8
1982	21.6	29.4	3.2	10.7	14.9	7.6	4.2	10.8
1983	21.6	32.4	3.4	11.9	15.1	8.3	3.9	11.8
1984	21.6	33.9	3.2	12.8	15.3	8.4	4.0	12.4
1985	21.8	37.5	3.1	14.1	15.3	9.2	4.1	13.9
1986	22.5	41.1	3.1	15.1	15.7	10.1	4.7	15.5
1987	23.1	45.1	3.2	16.1	15.6	11.1	4.8	16.6
1988	22.9	48.7	3.2	17.1	15.5	11.7	4.7	18.3
1989	23.5	54.5	3.1	18.6	15.7	13.8	4.6	21.5
1990	25.2	64.9	3.2	21.5	17.2	17.6	4.6	25.4

NOTES: Data excludes territories and possessions. Detail may not add to totals due to rounding. Excludes premium and per capita amounts and state expenditures not eligible for federal matching funds.

SOURCE: U.S.Department of Health and Human Services, Health Care Financing Administration, Medicaid Statistics Branch.

Table 3.3

Medicare and Medicaid Benefits, Medicare Enrollments, and Medicaid Recipients by State and Territory (Millions of dollars and thousands of persons)

States and territories	Medicare 1989		Medicaid 1990	
	Benefits paid	Number of persons enrolled	Benefits paid	Unduplicated count of recipients
Total	$94,300	33,579	$64,859	25,255
Alabama	1,278	573	609	352
Alaska	71	23	139	39
Arizona*	1,321	480	0	NA
Arkansas	952	386	599	264
California	9,827	3,211	6,507	3,624
Colorado	789	346	516	191
Connecticut	1,317	462	1,205	250
Delaware	235	86	123	41
District of Columbia	380	78	246	93
Florida	6,769	2,274	2,361	1,038
Georgia	1,989	715	2,076	651
Hawaii	234	122	191	85
Idaho	288	129	162	55
Illinois	4,531	1,516	2,424	1,067
Indiana	1,886	749	1,343	348
Iowa	1,045	452	620	240
Kansas	870	359	491	194
Kentucky	1,398	526	977	468
Louisiana	1,681	522	1,315	585
Maine	450	180	432	133
Maryland	1,874	528	1,090	330
Massachusetts	2,586	858	2,730	591
Michigan	3,938	1,209	2,195	1,048
Minnesota	1,053	579	1,410	380
Mississippi	933	361	586	433
Missouri	2,115	771	897	448
Montana	273	115	171	61
Nebraska	486	235	309	119
Nevada	364	131	149	47
New Hampshire	298	134	243	45
New Jersey	3,317	1,078	2,298	567
New Mexico	397	173	275	130
New York	8,277	2,492	11,877	2,329
North Carolina	1,982	867	1,426	563
North Dakota	245	98	194	49
Ohio	4,488	1,517	3,132	1,221
Oklahoma	1,189	444	688	273
Oregon	816	413	519	227
Pennsylvania	6,415	1,926	2,883	1,177
Rhode Island	344	157	442	117
South Carolina	859	430	743	317
South Dakota	234	109	166	49
Tennessee	1,856	678	1,163	613
Texas	5,111	1,778	2,781	1,442
Utah	364	154	247	108
Vermont	166	73	153	60

Continued

Virginia	1,882	703	985	379
Washington	1,494	600	952	448
West Virginia	723	304	361	250
Wisconsin	1,738	704	1,248	393
Wyoming	129	50	59	29
U.S. territories and possessions	448	429	150	1,300
Foreign countries	29	264	NA	NA

*Arizona operates a demonstration program instead of a regular program.

NOTE: Detail may not add to totals due to rounding and distributions by state are estimated.

SOURCE: U.S. Department of Health and Human Services, Health Care Financing Administration.

Table 3.4

Per Capita Personal Health Care Expenditures for Persons 65 Years and More by Age, Type of Service, and Source of Payment (1987)

| Age | Total | Source of funds | | | |
		Private	Medicare	Medicaid	Other
65 years or more	$5,360	$2,004	$2,391	$ 645	$321
65–69 years	3,728	1,430	1,849	245	204
70–74 years	4,424	1,564	2,234	357	268
75–79 years	5,455	1,843	2,685	569	358
80–84 years	6,717	2,333	3,023	908	453
85 years and more	9,178	3,631	3,215	1,742	591
Hospital care					
65 years or more	2,248	333	1,566	110	239
65–69 years	1,682	312	1,144	67	158
70–74 years	2,062	327	1,431	93	212
75–79 years	2,536	341	1,786	127	283
80–84 years	2,935	355	2,070	161	348
85 years and more	3,231	376	2,246	198	411
Physicians' services					
65 years or more	1,107	393	671	17	26
65–69 years	974	380	558	14	22
70–74 years	1,086	389	655	17	25
75–79 years	1,191	398	745	19	29
80–84 years	1,246	407	789	20	31
85 years and more	1,262	420	792	20	31
Nursing home care					
65 years or more	1,085	634	19	395	38
65–69 years	165	94	5	60	6
70–74 years	360	205	11	131	13
75–79 years	802	461	22	292	28
80–84 years	1,603	927	37	584	56
85 years and more	3,738	2,191	56	1,361	131
Other personal health care					
65 years or more	920	644	135	123	18
65–69 years	907	644	142	103	18
70–74 years	916	644	137	117	18
75–79 years	825	644	133	130	18
80–84 years	934	644	128	144	18
85 years and more	947	645	121	164	18

NOTE: Hospital care and physicians' services include both inpatient and outpatient care.
SOURCE: Health Care Financing Administration, HCFA Review, Summer 1989.

Table 3.5

Expenditures of State Health Agencies and Local Health Departments by Type of Expenditure (Fiscal Year 1989) (Thousands of dollars)

States and territories	Total public health expenditures	Direct SHA expenditures	SHA inter-governmental grants to LHDs	Additional expenditures of LHDs
Total	$11,814,903	$7,766,236	$1,738,899	$2,309,768
Alabama	177,214	94,445	37,796	44,973
Alaska	41,364E	37,377	1,584	2,403E
Arizona	389,911	159,963	9,392	220,556
Arkansas	84,087	84,087	—	—
California	1,045,700E	530,685	375,564	139,451E
Colorado	146,090	117,008	4,403	24,679
Connecticut	110,618	80,159	7,763	22,696
Delaware	59,470	59,470	—	—
District of Columbia	133,763	133,763	—	—
Florida	424,076	171,950	252,126	—
Georgia	279,027	180,266	53,501	45,260
Hawaii	258,867	250,856	7,529	482
Idaho	31,736E	20,043	3,226	8,467E
Illinois	373,740E	165,849	42,932	164,959E
Indiana	165,164	122,836	8,218	34,110
Iowa	84,723	61,319	5,084	18,320
Kansas	71,079E	45,925	8,947	16,207E
Kentucky	174,462	86,754	37,735	49,973
Louisiana	129,377E	125,740	2,280	1,357E
Maine	32,205E	29,845	1,360	1,000E
Maryland	807,002E	703,069	102,743	1,190E
Massachusetts	326,417E	302,106	4,799	19,512E
Michigan	529,616	190,125	161,923	177,568
Minnesota	212,868	75,578	23,664	113,626
Mississippi	110,822	79,794	31,028	—
Missouri	188,895	76,695	51,007	61,193
Montana	*	*	*	*
Nebraska	36,384E	30,641	738	5,005E
Nevada	39,036	20,515	2,270	16,251
New Hampshire	31,942E	25,437	—	6,505E
New Jersey	301,015	197,546	27,064	76,405
New Mexico	50,184	49,034	—	1,150
New York	1,150,259E	718,996	140,491	290,772E
North Carolina	321,952	135,372	49,032	137,548
North Dakota	27,804	18,258	2,704	6,842
Ohio	320,789E	149,998	49,376	121,415E
Oklahoma	112,495	53,275	45,096	14,124
Oregon	70,243E	38,010	12,565	19,668E
Pennsylvania	352,798	275,865	30,556	46,377
Rhode Island	40,790	40,790	—	—
South Carolina	212,584E	177,672	25,121	9,791E
South Dakota	23,648E	21,925	U	1,723E
Tennessee	224,144E	159,077	20,834	44,233E
Texas	550,158	410,885	33,901	105,372
Utah	82,955	47,770	17,411	17,774
Vermont	23,017	23,017	—	—
Virginia	219,883	219,883	—	—
Washington	177,804	69,037	22,747	86,020

Continued

Table 3.5 (Continued)

States and territories	Total public health expenditures	Direct SHA expenditures	SHA inter-governmental grants to LHDs	Additional expenditures of LHDs
West Virginia	181,860E	162,215	6,312	13,333E
Wisconsin	126,233E	67,483	13,608	45,142E
Wyoming	16,400	15,716	—	684
American Samoa	*	*	*	*
Guam	5,834	5,834	—	—
Puerto Rico	*	*	*	*
Virgin Islands	*	*	*	*

*Data have been estimated for the SHAs in Montana, American Samoa, Puerto Rico, and the Virgin Islands, which did not report to the Public Health Foundation for fiscal year 1989. Estimated data have been included in the totals.
E = Estimated by the respondent.
— = Zero or no data.
U = Data reported as unobtainable by the respondent.
NOTE: The data in this table relate only to expenditures of official state health agencies and local health departments. The public health expenditures of other agencies such as separate mental health authorities, environmental agencies, and hospital authorities are not reflected in the public health foundation's data base.
SOURCE: Public Health Foundation, 1989.

Table 3.6

Hospital and Medical Expenditures under Workers' Compensation (Millions)

Year	Total	State and local	Federal
1965	$ 799	$ 787	$ 12
1966	910	897	13
1967	1,012	996	15
1968	1,147	1,130	17
1969	1,263	1,244	19
1970	1,409	1,384	25
1971	1,441	1,414	27
1972	1,575	1,545	30
1973	1,884	1,848	35
1974	2,176	2,133	43
1975	2,436	2,371	61
1976	2,758	2,685	73
1977	3,191	3,112	79
1978	3,682	3,585	97
1979	4,541	4,424	117
1980	5,151	5,012	140
1981	5,695	5,536	159
1982	4,500	4,600	200
1983	5,400	5,100	300
1984	6,100	5,800	300
1985	7,000	6,700	300
1986	7,800	7,500	300
1987	8,900	8,600	300
1988	9,968	9,668	300

NOTES: For 1970 and succeeding years data include federal "black lung" benefits. Detail may not add to totals due to rounding.
SOURCE: U.S. Department of Health and Human Services, Health Care Financing Administration.

Chapter 4

MEDICAL CARE COSTS

◆ National Health Expenditures (NHE)

Total health care spending, represented by national health expenditures, includes both private and public expenditures for personal health care, medical research, construction of medical facilities, administrative and insurance costs, and government-sponsored public health programs.

National health spending reached $666.2 billion in 1990, a 10 percent increase over 1989, compared to 10.4 percent the previous year. Public spending amounted to 42 percent of all health care costs in 1990, slightly less than in 1989. (Table 4.1)

In 1960, NHE constituted 5.3 percent of the gross national product (GNP). It has increased steadily over the years, reaching 12.2 percent in 1990. (Tables 4.2 and 4.3)

Hospital care, totaling $256 billion in 1990, continued to represent the largest share of personal health spending (43.8 percent). The cost of physicians' services was the next highest at $125.7 billion. (Table 4.1)

According to HCFA, U.S. nursing home care in 1990 cost $53.1 billion. Medicare contributed only $800 million to this total. Medicaid paid nearly half ($19.3 billion) of these expenses, making it a de facto long-term care financing program. The remaining cost of financing long-term care fell almost exclusively on the patients and their families ($23.9 billion). Private long-term care insurance, still in its infancy, paid only $500 million.

The U.S. Department of Commerce predicts that NHE will reach $756.3 billion in 1991. The Department indicates that hospital spending is expected to rise 11.1 percent to $286 billion and physicians' services will soar to $148 billion in 1991, a 12.4 increase over 1990. It further predicts that if trends persist, health costs will rise 12 to 15 percent annually for five consecutive years.

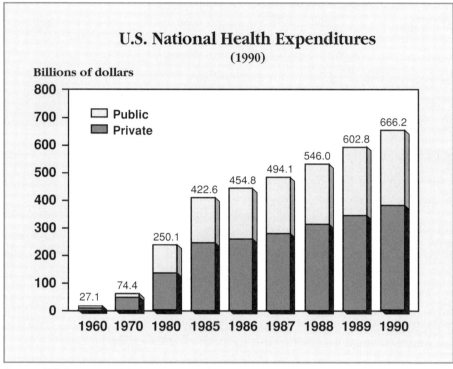

SOURCE: U.S. Department of Health and Human Services, Health Care Financing Administration.

Personal Health Care Expenditures

The personal health care expenditures (PHCE) figure ($585.3 billion in 1990), accounted for 87.9 percent of the NHE; it represents private and public spending for direct health and medical services to individuals.

1990 PHCE increased 10.5 percent over $529.9 billion in 1989. This is due to 4 factors: economywide price inflation, industry-specific price inflation, population, and intensity. Inflation and industry-specific price inflation together accounted for 69 percent of the increase, while population accounted for 10 percent, and intensity, 21 percent. Intensity may be defined as anything that causes changes in use per capita expenditure.

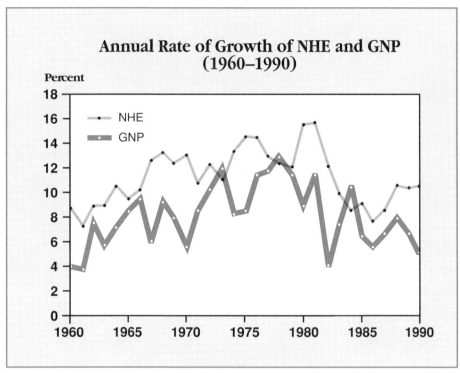

SOURCES: U.S. Department of Health and Human Services, Health Care Financing Administration and the U.S. Department of Commerce, Survey of Current Business.

Factors Affecting Growth of Personal Health Care Expenditures (1985–1990)
(Percent)

Factors	1985	1986	1987	1988	1989	1990
Prices	61	52	52	67	65	69
Population	11	11	9	10	9	10
Intensity	28	37	39	23	26	21
Total	100	100	100	100	100	100

SOURCE: U.S. Department of Health and Human Services, Health Care Financing Administration.

The PHCE includes expenditures for hospital care, professional services, drugs and medical sundries, and nursing home care. Expenditures for medical research, construction of medical facilities, public health activities such as disease prevention and control, and the net cost of health insurance are not included in the total.

Per capita expenditures were $2,566 in 1990, 9.3 percent more than the 1989 figure of $2,346. (Table 4.2)

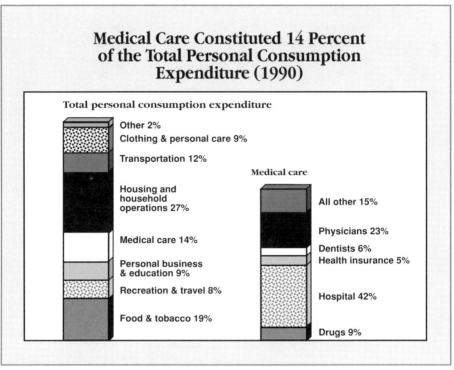

Medical Care Constituted 14 Percent of the Total Personal Consumption Expenditure (1990)

Total personal consumption expenditure

Other 2%
Clothing & personal care 9%

Transportation 12%

Medical care

Housing and household operations 27%

All other 15%

Physicians 23%

Medical care 14%

Dentists 6%
Health insurance 5%

Personal business & education 9%

Recreation & travel 8%

Hospital 42%

Food & tobacco 19%

Drugs 9%

SOURCE: U.S. Department of Commerce, Survey of Current Business.

The largest portion (79.5 percent) of the personal health care dollar derives from third-party sources. Private health insurance, philanthropy, industry, and the government paid $529.6 billion of all expenditures for personal health care in 1990.

Personal consumption expenditures. Personal consumption expenditures (PCE) is a measure of health expenditures published by the U.S. Department of Commerce rather than by HCFA. It measures private medical care payments. Monies from three government programs (Medicare, Workers' Compensation, and Temporary Disability Insurance) are treated as transfer payments and are included. PCE and PHCE differ because different accounting practices are used for each. PCE for 1990 was $536.1 billion, which represents 14.7 percent of the total spent by Americans on all personal needs, compared to 10.7 percent a decade earlier. As a proportion of the public's disposable income, these expenditures were 13.6 percent in 1990, up from 13 percent in 1989. (Table 4.7)

Consumer Price Index

The consumer price index (CPI) measures the average change in the prices paid by urban consumers for a fixed market basket of consumption goods and services ranging from Sunkist oranges to Sun Microsystems computers.

The CPI compares what the market basket of goods and services costs consumers this month with the same market basket costs a month, a year, or even 10 years ago.

According to the 1990 CPI, medical prices increased by 9.0 percent from 1989, compared to a 5.4 percent increase for all items. (Table 4.8)

Individual components of the medical care index have differed in their rates of increase, but hospital room rates have risen most rapidly.

Hospital Statistics

Community hospital statistics. In 1989, the average expense to the hospital for treating a patient in a community hospital was $636.96 per inpatient day, almost a 9 percent increase over 1988. On a state-by-state basis, the average cost per inpatient day in 1989 varied considerably from a low of $378.21 in Montana to a high of $995.90 in Alaska. (Table 4.9)

In 1989, the average length of time a patient remained in a community hospital was 7.2 days, the same as one year earlier. The average length of stay varied by area, from a low of 5.6 days in Oregon to a high of 10.7 in North Dakota. The average cost of a stay in a community hospital in 1989 was $4,587.87, a 9 percent increase over 1988.

Operating costs of community hospitals were $184.9 billion in 1989, which is a 9.6 percent increase over the $168.7 billion spent in 1988. The American Hospital Association (AHA) reports that labor costs reached $99 billion in 1989, representing 54 percent of total community hospital expenditures.

During the past decade, hospitals have broadened the range of alternative services they offer. These changes reflect advances in technology, greater emphasis on nonacute care as a result of new payment systems, and medical care which allows a greater choice for the patient.

Freestanding outpatient surgery centers. As one of the nation's fastest-growing groups of health care providers, freestanding outpatient surgery centers, often referred to as surgi-centers, are expected to number 1,510 in 1991. More than 2.5 million surgical procedures were performed in 1,381 such facilities in 1990. It is estimated that more than 3 million procedures will take place in 1991.

Psychiatric hospital statistics. The nation's 741 nonfederal mental hospitals (161,000 beds), were 87 percent occupied in 1989, with an 8 percent decrease in admissions between 1979 and 1989. There was a sharp decline in the average length of stay, from 120 days in 1979 to 70 days in 1989. Psychiatric hospitals have increased in number (200 in the past 10 years), and admissions rose almost 25 percent during the 10-year period. According to *Hospital Statistics*, it cost more than $12 billion to operate facilities devoted to mental health care in the United States in 1989.

Semiprivate room charges. A final survey conducted by HIAA shows that as of January 1990, the national average room and board charge to the patient for a semiprivate room was $297 per day, a 12.5 percent increase over January 1989. (Table 4.11) Survey results are based on responses from 1,414 nongovernmental short-term general hospitals nationwide. The highest daily average rate of $456 was in Connecticut. The lowest rate was in Puerto Rico, at $158 per day.

Professional Fees

Surgical charges. Surgical charges vary considerably by geographical region and by metropolitan and nonmetropolitan areas. Table 4.12, containing data from a 1990 survey by *Medical Economics*, shows fees for a number of common surgical procedures and emergency medical procedures across the United States.

The Division of Health Care Statistics of the National Center for Health Statistics (NCHS) listed the most frequently performed surgical procedures in 1989 as follows:

Procedure	Number in thousands	Per 100,000 population
Total	23,370	9,479.0
Episiotomy	1,704	691.0
Cardiac catheterization	958	388.4
Cesarean section	953	380.4
Repair OB (birth) laceration	762	309.1
Artificial rupture membranes	654	265.1
Excision/destruction of lesion	542	219.7
Hysterectomy	541	219.3
Arthroplasty/repair joints	534	216.7
Cholecystectomy	504	204.2
Open reduction of fracture	479	194.2
Puncture of vessel	469	190.1
Oophorectomy and salpingo-oophorectomy	421	170.6
Occlusion of fallopian tubes	389	157.6
Prostatectomy	376	152.6
Coronary bypass	368	149.3
Excision of intervertebral disc and spinal fusion	355	144.1
Division of adhesions	329	133.4
Operations on muscles, tendons, and bursa	312	126.3

The HIAA Prevailing Healthcare Charges System collects data on charges by geographical areas of the United States. Charges for selected surgical procedures for 1991 are shown below:

Procedure	New York City	Philadelphia	Atlanta	Chicago	Denver	Dallas	Los Angeles
Excision of breast lesion (lumpectomy)	$1,252	$ 595	$ 570	$ 612	$ 463	$ 581	$ 737
Cesarean section	4,789	2,285	2,408	2,337	2,203	1,982	2,554
Hysterectomy	4,997	2,443	2,176	2,516	1,707	1,905	2,622
Oophorectomy	2,734	1,705	1,349	1,616	917	1,131	1,629
Salpingo-oophorectomy	3,318	1,798	1,314	1,589	925	1,263	1,328
Coronary bypass (triple)	8,189	6,118	4,656	5,902	4,499	2,461	6,375
Appendectomy	1,901	1,039	958	1,126	885	938	1,268
Cholecystectomy	3,048	1,535	1,498	1,740	1,509	1,506	1,944
Vasectomy	670	464	395	451	347	367	486
Prostatectomy (retro-pubic)	3,268	1,938	2,256	1,829	1,533	1,447	2,444

The 1991 Health Insurance Association of America's Surgical Prevailing Healthcare Charges System is copyrighted and is available by subscription only to certain types of organizations.

Physician fees. Physician fees vary considerably by type of practice and specialty, type of visit, and region of the United States. (Table 4.13) In 1989, the median charges for an initial office visit and an office revisit were highest for specialists and for physicians practicing in the western states. According to a continuing survey done by *Medical Economics*, physicians' fees historically have risen at a higher rate than the CPI. The all-services index of the CPI increased by 5.4 percent in 1990, while physicians' fees rose 7.1 percent.

◆ The Cost of Mental Illness and Drug Abuse

Mental illness and drug abuse in the United States cost an estimated $105 billion in 1989, which represented approximately 17 percent of the 1989 NHE ($604.1 billion).

Type of Psychiatric Treatment or Psychotherapy Session	Median Fee
Individual psychotherapy in office (45-50 minutes)	$101
Individual psychotherapy in hospital (45-50 minutes)	120
Family therapy session	151
Psychiatric diagnostic interview	130
Initial consultation in office, comprehensive	131
Initial consultation in hospital, comprehensive	151
Group psychotherapy, per person	50

SOURCE: Medical Economics, October 1, 1990. Copyright © 1990. Reprinted by permission.

In 1989, nearly 2 million Americans of all ages were beset with some form of mental disorder. A Health Interview Survey by NCHS in 1989 found that more males than females were diagnosed as schizophrenic and more females were afflicted with affective psychosis, the most prevalent mental disorder in the United States.

There were 372,000 persons of both sexes and all ages diagnosed with affective psychosis in 1989. At the same time, 145,000 people between the ages of 15 and 44 years were diagnosed as schizophrenic. (Table 4.16)

According to the National Mental Health Association, 68 percent of people with diagnosable mental disorders receive some ambulatory medical treatment, 22 percent actually visit a mental health specialist, and 10 percent consult a general family practitioner. A large majority of the recorded psychiatric admissions each year are actually readmissions.

In a 1990 survey of employers, HIAA found that the majority of conventional, PPO, and HMO plans cover outpatient and inpatient mental health, drug treatment, and treatment for alcohol problems.

◆ The Cost of Having a Baby

Most group medical expense plans cover maternity care. Maternity coverage is often mandated by state law, and more than 95 percent of employees under employer-sponsored group policies underwritten by commercial insurance companies have maternity benefits. HIAA's Employer Survey 1990 reported that more than 95 percent of PPOs, IPAs, HMOs, and point-of-service plans provide well-baby and well-child care.

In 1989, HIAA conducted a national survey to determine the costs of normal and Cesarean births. The average cost of a vaginal delivery in a hospital delivery room was $4,334. The Midwest reported the lowest cost of $4,149 and the Northeast reported the highest, $4,456. (Table 4.15)

The number of Cesarean deliveries increased from 17 percent of all births in 1980 to 25 percent in 1989. Cesarean births have remained at almost 4 percent of the total surgical procedures ever since. The average cost of an uncomplicated Cesarean delivery in the United States was $7,186 in 1989.

◆ Medical Costs Resulting from Accidents

The economic losses that result from various types of accidents are shown in Table 4.19. Medical expense costs incurred through accidents totaled $143.4 billion in 1989.

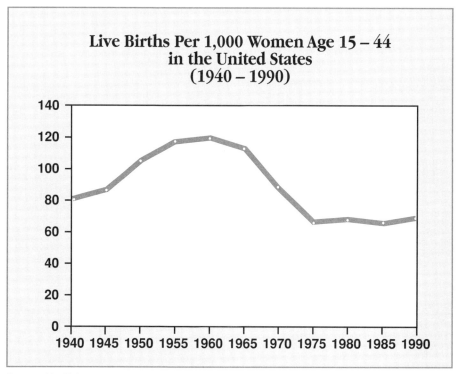

Live Births Per 1,000 Women Age 15 – 44 in the United States (1940 – 1990)

SOURCE: Health Insurance Association of America.

◆ International Health Care Expenditures

According to the Organization for Economic Cooperation and Development (OECD), the United States allocates a greater proportion of its gross domestic product (GDP) to health care than any other country. (GDP differs from GNP in that it does not include net foreign investment income.) In 1989, the United States spent $2,354 on each citizen, while Canada spent only $1,683, West Germany only $1,232, and the United Kingdom $836 in American dollars.

The United States spent more on health care in 1989 than any other country; however, since 1970 per capita health costs have grown faster in Canada, France, and the United Kingdom.

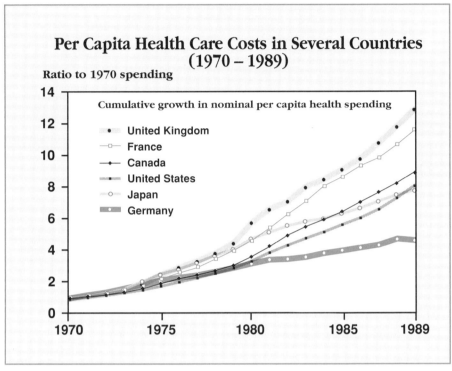

Per Capita Health Care Costs in Several Countries
(1970 – 1989)

Ratio to 1970 spending

Cumulative growth in nominal per capita health spending

- United Kingdom
- France
- Canada
- United States
- Japan
- Germany

SOURCE: Health Affairs, Spring 1991 (Organization for Economic Cooperation and Development).

Table 4.1

National Health Expenditures by Source of Funds and Type of Expenditure (1989–1990) (Billions)

Year and type of expenditure	Total	All private funds	Private Consumer Total	Out of pocket	Private insurance	Other	Government Total	Federal	State and local
1989									
National health expenditures	$602.8	$350.2	$322.5	$126.1	$196.4	$27.7	$252.6	$175.0	$77.6
Health services and supplies	582.1	342.1	322.5	126.1	196.4	19.6	240.0	165.2	74.8
Personal health care	529.9	314.7	295.7	126.1	169.6	19.0	215.2	158.8	56.3
Hospital care	232.6	107.9	95.3	12.1	83.2	12.6	124.6	93.7	30.9
Physician services	113.6	74.2	74.1	21.3	52.8	0.0	39.4	31.6	7.8
Dental services	31.6	30.8	30.8	17.3	13.5	—	0.7	0.4	0.3
Other professional services	27.1	21.5	18.6	7.9	10.6	3.0	5.6	4.2	1.3
Home health care	5.6	1.4	1.0	0.7	0.4	0.4	4.2	3.3	0.9
Drugs and other medical nondurables	50.6	45.5	45.5	38.1	7.3	—	5.1	2.5	2.6
Vision products and other medical durables	11.4	9.0	9.0	7.8	1.2	—	2.4	2.1	0.3
Nursing home care	47.7	22.3	21.4	20.8	0.5	0.9	25.4	16.4	9.0
Other personal health care	9.7	2.1	—	—	—	2.1	7.7	4.5	3.2
Program administration and net cost of private health insurance	33.9	27.3	26.8	—	26.8	0.5	6.6	4.3	2.3
Government public health activities	18.3	—	—	—	—	—	18.3	2.1	16.2
Research and construction	20.7	8.2	—	—	—	8.2	12.5	9.7	2.8
Research	11.0	0.8	—	—	—	0.8	10.3	8.9	1.4
Construction	9.6	7.4	—	—	—	7.4	2.2	0.8	1.4
1990									
National health expenditures	$666.2	$383.6	$352.9	$136.1	$216.8	$30.6	$282.6	$195.4	$87.3
Health services and supplies	643.4	374.8	352.9	136.1	216.8	21.8	268.6	184.3	84.3
Personal health care	585.3	343.5	322.2	136.1	186.1	21.3	241.8	177.2	64.6
Hospital care	256.0	116.0	102.2	12.8	89.4	13.8	140.0	104.6	35.3
Physician services	125.7	81.7	81.7	23.5	58.2	0.0	43.9	35.1	8.8
Dental services	34.0	33.1	33.1	18.0	15.1	—	0.9	0.5	0.4
Other professional services	31.6	25.2	21.5	8.8	12.8	3.6	6.4	4.9	1.6
Home health care	6.9	1.8	1.3	0.8	0.5	0.5	5.1	4.1	1.0
Drugs and other medical nondurables	54.6	48.5	48.5	40.2	8.3	—	6.1	3.0	3.1
Vision products and other medical durables	12.1	9.4	9.4	8.2	1.3	—	2.7	2.4	0.3
Nursing home care	53.1	25.5	24.4	23.9	0.6	1.0	27.7	17.2	10.5
Other personal health care	11.3	2.2	—	—	—	2.2	9.1	5.5	3.5
Program administration and net cost of private health insurance	38.7	31.2	30.7	—	30.7	0.6	7.5	4.8	2.7

Continued

Table 4.1 *(Continued)*

Year and type of expenditure	Total	Private All private funds	Private Total	Consumer Out of pocket	Consumer Private insurance	Other	Government Total	Government Federal	Government State and local
Government public health activities	19.3	—	—	—	—	—	19.3	2.3	17.0
Research and construction	22.8	8.8	—	—	—	8.8	14.0	11.0	3.0
Research	12.4	0.8	—	—	—	0.8	11.5	10.0	1.5
Construction	10.4	8.0	—	—	—	8.0	2.5	1.0	1.5

NOTES: 0.0 denotes less than $50 million. Research and development expenditures of drug companies and other manufacturers and providers of medical equipment and supplies are excluded from "research expenditures," but are included in the expenditure class in which the product falls. Numbers may not add to totals because of rounding. Dashes indicate no data are available.

SOURCE: Health Care Financing Administration, Office of the Actuary: Data from the Office of National Health Statistics.

Table 4.2

National Health Expenditures in Aggregate, Per Capita, Percent Distribution, and Percent Growth by Source of Funds (1960–1990)

Item	1960	1970	1980	1985	1986	1987	1988	1989	1990
				Amount in billions					
National health expenditures	$ 27.1	$ 74.4	$ 250.1	$ 422.6	$ 454.8	$ 494.1	$ 546.0	$ 602.8	$ 666.2
Private	20.5	46.7	145.0	247.7	264.6	285.7	318.9	350.2	383.6
Public	6.7	27.7	105.2	174.8	190.2	208.4	227.1	252.6	282.6
Federal	2.9	17.7	72.0	123.6	133.1	144.0	156.7	175.0	195.4
State and local	3.7	9.9	33.2	51.2	57.2	64.4	70.5	77.6	87.3
				Number in millions					
U.S. population	190.1	214.9	235.3	247.2	249.6	252.0	254.5	257.0	259.6
				Amount in billions					
Gross national product	$515.0	$1,015.0	$2,732.0	$4,015.0	$4,232.0	$4,516.0	$4,874.0	$5,201.0	$5,465.0
				Per capita amount					
National health expenditures	$143.0	$346.0	$1,063.0	$1,710.0	$1,822.0	$1,961.0	$2,146.0	$2,346.0	$2,566.0
Private	108.0	217.0	616.0	1,003.0	1,060.0	1,134.0	1,253.0	1,363.0	1,478.0
Public	35.0	129.0	447.0	707.0	762.0	827.0	893.0	983.0	1,089.0
Federal	15.0	83.0	306.0	500.0	533.0	571.0	616.0	681.0	753.0
State and local	20.0	46.0	141.0	207.0	229.0	255.0	277.0	302.0	336.0
				Percent distribution					
National health expenditures	100.0	100.0	100.0	100.0	100.0	100.0	100.0	100.0	100.0
Private	75.5	62.8	58.0	58.6	58.2	57.8	57.4	58.1	57.6
Public	24.5	37.2	42.0	41.4	41.8	42.2	41.6	41.9	42.4
Federal	10.7	23.9	28.8	29.2	29.2	29.1	27.7	29.0	29.3
State and local	13.9	10.3	13.3	12.1	12.6	13.0	12.9	12.9	13.1
				Percent of gross national product					
National health expenditures	5.3	7.3	9.2	10.5	10.7	10.9	11.2	11.6	12.2
				Average annual percent growth from previous years					
National health expenditures		10.6	12.9	11.1	7.6	8.6	10.5	10.4	10.5
Private		8.6	12.0	11.3	6.8	8.0	11.6	9.8	9.5
Public		13.3	14.3	10.7	8.8	9.5	9.0	11.2	11.9
Federal		19.8	15.0	11.4	7.6	8.2	8.8	11.7	11.7
State and local		10.2	12.8	9.0	11.8	12.6	9.5	10.1	12.5
U.S. population		1.2	0.9	1.0	1.0	1.0	1.0	1.0	1.0
Gross national product		7.0	10.4	8.0	5.4	6.7	7.9	6.7	5.1

NOTE: Numbers and percents may not add to totals because of rounding.

SOURCE: U.S. Department of Health and Human Services, Health Care Financing Administration, Office of the Actuary.

Table 4.3

National Health Expenditure and Gross National Product (1950–1990)

Year	National health expenditure amount (billions)	Annual rate of growth (percent)	Gross national product amount (billions)	Annual rate of growth (percent)	National health expenditure as percent of GNP
1950	$ 12.7	12.2	$ 288.0	10.7	4.4
1955	17.7	7.0	406.0	7.0	4.4
1960	27.1	8.7	515.0	3.9	5.3
1961	29.1	7.1	534.0	3.6	5.4
1962	31.6	8.8	575.0	7.6	5.5
1963	34.4	8.9	607.0	5.6	5.7
1964	38.1	10.5	650.0	7.1	5.9
1965	41.6	9.4	705.0	8.5	5.9
1966	45.9	10.2	772.0	9.5	5.9
1967	51.7	12.6	816.0	5.8	6.3
1968	58.5	13.2	898.0	9.3	6.6
1969	65.7	12.4	964.0	7.9	6.8
1970	74.4	13.1	1,016.0	5.4	7.3
1971	82.3	10.6	1,103.0	8.6	7.5
1972	92.4	12.3	1,213.0	10.0	7.6
1973	102.5	10.9	1,659.0	12.1	7.5
1974	116.1	13.3	1,473.0	8.3	7.9
1975	132.9	14.5	1,598.0	8.5	8.3
1976	152.2	14.5	1,783.0	11.5	8.5
1977	172.0	13.0	1,991.0	11.7	8.6
1978	193.4	12.4	2,250.0	13.0	8.6
1979	216.6	12.0	2,508.0	11.5	8.6
1980	250.1	15.5	2,732.0	8.9	9.1
1981	288.5	15.8	3,053.0	11.7	9.5
1982	323.8	12.2	3,166.0	3.7	10.2
1983	356.1	9.9	3,406.0	7.6	10.5
1984	386.9	8.6	3,772.0	10.7	10.3
1985	422.6	9.2	4,015.0	6.4	10.5
1986	454.8	7.6	4,232.0	5.4	10.7
1987	494.1	8.6	4,516.0	6.7	10.9
1988	546.0	10.5	4,874.0	7.9	11.2
1989	602.8	10.4	5,201.0	6.7	11.6
1990	666.2	10.5	5,463.0	5.0	12.2

SOURCE: U.S. Department of Health and Human Services, Health Care Financing Administration.

Table 4.4

Personal Health Care Expenditures by Source of Payment (1960 – 1990) (Billions)

Year	Total personal health care expenditure	Consumer					Federal		
		Consumer payments	Out of pocket	Private health insurance	Other private funds	State and local	Federal	Medicare	Medicaid
1960	$ 23.9	$ 18.4	$ 13.4	$ 5.1	$ 0.4	$ 2.9	$ 2.1	$ 0.0	$ 0.0
1961	25.3	19.4	13.7	5.7	0.5	3.2	2.3	0.0	0.0
1962	27.3	21.1	14.6	6.3	0.5	3.3	2.6	0.0	0.0
1963	29.8	22.8	15.9	6.9	0.5	3.7	2.8	0.0	0.0
1964	32.8	25.5	17.7	7.8	0.6	3.9	2.8	0.0	0.0
1965	35.6	27.7	19.0	8.7	0.8	4.3	2.9	0.0	0.0
1966	39.4	28.4	19.3	9.1	0.9	4.8	2.9	1.6	1.3
1967	44.7	28.5	18.9	9.6	1.0	5.5	7.9	4.9	3.0
1968	51.0	32.1	21.2	10.9	1.1	6.0	9.3	5.9	3.4
1969	57.1	35.9	23.1	12.9	1.5	6.7	10.8	6.8	4.0
1970	64.9	40.8	25.6	15.2	1.7	7.8	12.3	7.2	5.1
1971	71.3	44.1	27.1	17.0	1.9	8.5	14.5	8.1	6.4
1972	79.4	48.5	29.8	18.7	2.1	9.7	16.8	8.8	8.0
1973	88.6	54.1	32.9	21.2	2.5	11.2	19.2	10.2	9.1
1974	101.6	61.1	35.6	25.1	3.0	12.4	23.4	12.8	10.6
1975	116.6	68.4	38.5	29.9	3.5	14.4	28.6	15.7	12.9
1976	132.8	77.6	42.5	35.1	4.1	14.6	33.4	18.9	14.5
1977	149.2	87.1	46.3	40.8	4.7	16.8	38.6	22.1	16.6
1978	167.2	96.7	49.9	46.7	5.5	18.6	44.3	25.8	18.5
1979	188.6	108.2	53.5	54.7	6.5	20.9	51.3	30.1	21.2
1980	219.4	124.6	59.5	65.3	7.6	23.6	61.2	36.4	24.8
1981	253.2	142.6	65.5	77.1	8.9	26.7	72.7	43.9	28.9
1982	286.4	160.4	71.9	88.5	10.1	29.5	81.9	51.4	30.7
1983	312.4	176.2	78.8	97.4	11.0	31.8	92.1	58.4	33.6
1984	338.6	191.4	85.1	106.4	11.4	34.1	100.4	64.4	36.0
1985	369.7	208.4	94.4	114.0	12.9	36.9	110.1	70.4	39.7
1986	398.2	222.7	97.4	125.2	13.5	41.7	118.6	75.7	42.9
1987	436.7	244.2	104.7	139.4	14.7	47.5	129.9	81.7	48.2
1988	482.8	273.4	119.3	154.1	16.8	50.9	140.5	88.5	52.1
1989	529.9	295.7	126.1	169.6	19.0	56.3	159.5	100.3	59.2
1990	585.3	322.2	136.1	186.1	21.3	64.6	180.2	108.9	71.3

SOURCE: U.S. Department of Health and Human Services, Health Care Financing Administration, unpublished data.

Table 4.5

Personal Consumption Expenditures by Type of Expenditure (1985–1989) (Billions)

	1985	1986	1987	1988	1989
Total expenditures	**$2,629.9**	**$2,797.4**	**$3,009.4**	**$3,238.2**	**$3,450.1**
Food and tobacco	503.8	533.6	566.4	599.6	636.9
Housing	403.3	434.2	468.9	502.3	533.9
Medical care	327.5	357.6	399.0	444.0	483.5
Drugs and sundries*	36.0	39.2	32.3	34.3	36.4
Physicians	73.5	80.6	94.0	106.1	113.0
Dentists	21.5	22.8	25.0	27.1	29.0
Private hospitals and sanitariums	140.2	152.4	166.3	182.9	201.1
Health insurance	21.6	22.4	25.3	27.7	29.6
Medical care and hospitalization	17.7	18.5	20.1	22.3	23.5
Income loss (disability)	2.3	2.5	2.6	2.7	2.9
Workers' Compensation	1.7	1.5	2.7	2.8	3.2
Transportation	359.5	366.3	379.7	407.5	425.7
Household operation	334.1	347.5	363.3	386.1	404.9
Recreation	185.7	201.2	223.2	245.1	264.4
Personal business	169.9	192.5	215.4	227.1	243.1
Clothing, accessories, and jewelry	193.3	207.2	222.3	240.0	257.8
Religious and welfare activities	57.1	62.9	68.1	75.9	82.9
Private education and research	43.3	46.6	50.9	57.7	64.3
Personal care	38.8	41.4	44.5	48.3	52.3
Foreign travel and other	13.1	6.5	7.7	4.4	0.4

*Drugs and sundries include ophthalmic products and orthopedic appliances.

SOURCE: U.S. Department of Commerce, Bureau of Economic Analysis, Survey of Current Business, July 1990.

Table 4.6

Personal Consumption Expenditures for Medical Care by Type of Service (1950–1990) (Billions)

Year	Total medical care	Hospital services	Physicians' services	Drugs, sundries, and appliances	Dentists' services	Net cost of health insurance	All other medical care
1950	$ 8.8	$ 2.1	$ 2.6	$ 2.2	$ 1.0	$ 0.3	$ 0.8
1955	13.4	3.4	3.8	3.0	1.5	0.6	1.1
1960	20.6	5.6	5.8	4.7	2.0	0.8	1.8
1965	31.6	8.9	8.5	6.4	2.8	1.3	3.7
1966	34.3	10.1	9.1	6.7	3.0	1.4	4.0
1967	37.1	11.8	10.0	7.0	3.4	1.3	3.7
1968	42.5	14.1	10.9	7.8	3.7	2.0	4.1
1969	48.3	17.0	12.4	8.6	4.3	1.9	4.1
1970	55.0	19.7	14.0	10.0	4.9	2.1	4.3
1971	60.9	23.2	15.3	10.5	5.1	2.6	4.2
1972	67.6	25.9	16.6	11.5	5.6	3.5	4.5
1973	75.1	28.8	18.4	12.5	6.6	3.6	5.2
1974	84.3	33.7	20.3	13.6	7.3	3.6	5.8
1975	96.9	40.1	23.5	14.9	8.2	3.2	7.0
1976	109.9	46.6	25.8	16.3	9.3	3.6	8.4
1977	126.5	53.3	29.6	17.4	10.3	5.4	10.4
1978	141.0	61.0	32.3	19.2	11.3	4.7	12.4
1979	160.6	70.0	36.3	21.6	12.3	5.6	14.8
1980	185.7	82.0	42.0	23.5	13.7	6.9	17.6
1981	217.3	96.8	49.0	25.8	16.1	7.6	22.0
1982	242.7	110.3	54.4	27.6	17.4	8.8	24.1
1983	266.5	119.6	61.1	30.3	18.5	11.0	25.8
1984	296.1	130.6	67.1	33.0	19.8	15.2	30.4
1985	327.5	140.2	73.5	36.0	21.5	21.6	34.7
1986	357.6	152.4	80.6	39.2	22.8	22.4	40.2
1987	399.0	166.3	94.0	41.7	25.0	25.3	46.6
1988	444.0	182.9	106.1	45.6	27.1	27.7	54.6
1989	483.5	201.1	113.0	49.2	29.0	29.6	61.7
1990	536.1	224.6	126.8	52.7	31.4	31.1	72.5

NOTES: The data exclude private expenditures in federal, state, city, and other government hospitals and nursing homes. In some cases, the sum of the items does not equal the "total medical care" shown because of rounding.

SOURCE: U.S. Department of Commerce, Bureau of Economic Analysis, Survey of Current Business, various issues.

Table 4.7

Personal Consumption Expenditures for Medical Care as Percent of Disposable Personal Income and as Percent of Total Personal Consumption Expenditures (1950–1990) (Billions)

Year	Personal consumption expenditures for medical care	Total personal consumption expenditures	Medical care as percent of total personal consumption expenditures	Disposable personal income	Medical care as percent of disposable income
1950	$ 8.8	$ 192.1	4.6	$ 207.5	4.3
1955	13.4	257.9	5.2	278.8	4.8
1960	20.6	330.7	6.2	358.9	5.7
1965	31.6	440.7	7.2	486.8	6.5
1970	55.0	640.0	8.6	715.6	7.7
1971	60.9	691.6	8.8	776.8	7.8
1972	67.6	757.6	9.0	839.6	8.1
1973	75.1	837.2	9.0	949.8	7.9
1974	84.3	916.5	9.2	1,038.3	8.1
1975	96.9	1,012.8	9.6	1,142.8	8.5
1976	109.9	1,129.3	9.7	1,252.6	8.8
1977	126.5	1,257.2	10.1	1,379.3	9.2
1978	141.0	1,403.5	10.0	1,151.2	12.2
1979	160.6	1,566.8	10.3	1,729.3	9.3
1980	185.7	1,732.6	10.7	1,917.9	9.7
1981	217.3	1,915.1	11.3	2,127.6	10.2
1982	242.7	2,050.7	11.8	2,261.4	10.7
1983	266.5	2,234.5	11.9	2,428.1	11.0
1984	296.1	2,430.5	12.2	2,668.6	11.1
1985	325.2	2,629.0	12.3	2,838.7	11.4
1986	357.6	2,797.4	12.8	3,013.3	11.8
1987	399.0	3,009.4	13.3	3,194.7	12.5
1988	444.0	3,238.2	13.7	3,479.2	12.8
1989	483.5	3,450.1	14.0	3,725.5	13.0
1990	536.1	3,657.3	14.7	3,946.1	13.6

NOTE: Includes all expenses for health insurance except loss of income type of coverage.

SOURCES: U.S. Department of Commerce, Bureau of Economic Analysis, Survey of Current Business, various issues, and Health Insurance Association of America.

Table 4.8

Annual Percent Change in Consumer Price Index (All urban consumers) (1969–1990)

Year	All items	All medical care items	Physicians' services	Dentists' fees	Hospital room	Prescription drugs	Medical care commodities
1969	5.5	8.2	7.0	7.2	13.6	1.3	0.9
1970	5.7	7.0	7.5	5.7	12.9	1.7	2.4
1971	4.4	7.4	7.0	6.4	12.3	0.0	1.7
1972	3.2	3.5	3.0	4.1	6.4	−0.4	0.2
1973	6.2	4.5	3.5	3.2	5.0	−0.2	0.2
1974	11.0	10.4	9.2	7.6	10.5	2.3	3.6
1975	9.1	12.6	12.1	10.4	17.1	6.2	8.3
1976	5.8	10.1	11.2	6.2	13.8	5.3	6.0
1977	6.5	9.9	9.3	7.6	11.5	6.1	6.5
1978	7.6	8.5	8.4	7.1	11.1	7.7	7.0
1979	11.3	9.8	9.1	8.3	11.3	7.8	7.1
1980	13.5	11.3	10.5	11.9	13.1	9.2	9.3
1981	10.3	10.7	11.0	9.6	14.9	11.4	11.0
1982	6.2	11.8	9.4	7.6	15.7	11.6	10.3
1983	3.2	8.7	7.8	6.8	11.3	11.0	8.6
1984	4.3	6.0	6.9	8.1	8.3	9.6	7.3
1985	3.6	6.1	5.9	6.2	5.9	9.5	7.2
1986	8.0	7.7	7.2	5.6	6.0	8.6	6.6
1987	3.6	6.6	7.3	6.8	7.2	8.0	6.7
1988	4.1	6.4	7.2	6.8	9.3	8.0	6.8
1989	4.8	7.7	7.4	6.3	10.3	8.7	7.8
1990	5.4	9.0	7.1	6.6	10.9	10.0	8.4

SOURCE: U.S. Department of Labor, Bureau of Labor Statistics, CPI detailed report, various issues.

Table 4.9

Community Hospital Statistics by State (1989)

State	Number of hospitals	Hospital beds	Occupancy rate	Admissions	Average cost to hospital per day*	Average length of hospital stay	Average cost to hospital per stay*
Total United States	5,455	933,318	66.2	31,116,048	$636.96	7.2	$4,587.87
Alabama	121	18,637	61.3	592,175	547.43	7.0	3,839.06
Alaska	17	1,263	48.9	38,771	995.90	5.8	5,858.53
Arizona	62	10,106	62.2	400,263	805.33	5.7	4,588.97
Arkansas	87	10,694	60.0	336,372	495.86	7.0	3,430.33
California	459	81,595	64.1	3,007,894	871.80	6.3	5,495.39
Colorado	71	9,706	63.8	332,725	689.35	6.8	4,681.27
Connecticut	36	9,771	76.6	355,898	763.37	7.7	5,821.92
Delaware	8	2,018	75.8	81,301	712.61	6.9	4,852.83
District of Columbia	12	4,693	79.8	173,800	844.49	7.9	6,600.12
Florida	229	50,334	61.1	1,612,615	717.60	7.0	4,968.11
Georgia	165	25,703	65.2	893,709	577.08	6.8	3,919.97
Hawaii	18	2,838	83.2	95,291	549.90	9.0	5,076.89
Idaho	43	3,191	55.2	92,547	494.72	7.0	3,515,13
Illinois	213	47,584	63.5	1,490,443	665.06	7.4	4,898.64
Indiana	112	21,995	59.7	713,120	614.78	6.7	4,091.41
Iowa	125	14,311	61.9	387,508	456.27	8.3	3,812.29
Kansas	137	11,884	55.8	305,749	476.70	7.9	3,745.34
Kentucky	108	15,784	61.3	533,374	520.45	6.6	3,420.23
Louisiana	142	18,894	56.8	609,596	658.12	6.4	4,190.08
Maine	39	4,515	71.8	146,694	523.66	8.1	4,207.26
Maryland	52	13,413	78.2	556,171	623.75	6.9	4,279.85
Massachusetts	103	22,217	75.5	800,379	729.80	7.6	5,558.43
Michigan	176	34,036	66.2	1,099,540	675.12	7.5	4,961.18
Minnesota	154	19,544	65.5	525,455	506.76	8.9	4,467.81
Mississippi	104	13,026	57.3	391,882	413.30	7.0	2,881.73
Missouri	136	24,397	62.8	745,594	624.03	7.5	4,644.01
Montana	56	4,595	61.4	104,505	378.21	9.9	3,711.32
Nebraska	91	8,816	56.2	185,844	441.60	9.7	4,282.79
Nevada	22	3,331	58.5	113,045	840.88	6.3	5,286.05
New Hampshire	28	3,474	66.8	124,087	613.74	6.8	4,169.77
New Jersey	93	28,445	79.3	1,116,288	567.92	7.4	4,196.11
New Mexico	39	4,339	58.9	153,873	682.80	6.1	4,064.42
New York	239	74,749	85.6	2,335,554	581.74	10.0	5,767.93
North Carolina	125	21,734	72.6	778,540	549.44	7.4	4,032.32
North Dakota	51	4,570	63.0	98,165	396.18	10.7	4,171.85
Ohio	191	44,123	64.7	1,529,054	668.75	6.8	4,511.77
Oklahoma	113	12,443	58.0	386,355	585.74	6.8	3,969.86
Oregon	71	8,072	58.2	306,876	742.55	5.6	4,143.45
Pennsylvania	238	52,089	71.6	1,780,251	629.13	7.6	4,773.67
Rhode Island	12	3,211	79.4	124,420	620.79	7.5	4,659.13
South Carolina	70	11,106	69.0	401,115	533.60	7.0	3,732.49
South Dakota	53	4,071	60.8	95,131	386.08	9.5	3,620.82
Tennessee	134	23,543	64.2	794,622	584.47	6.9	4,021.95
Texas	433	60,019	56.6	1,975,235	685.08	6.3	4,263.90
Utah	42	4,457	58.1	171,846	773.65	5.5	4,188.34
Vermont	16	1,760	65.3	57,703	556.41	7.3	4,009.54
Virginia	98	20,114	66.3	704,868	588.74	6.9	4,054.11
Washington	96	12,237	61.4	478,286	746.14	5.7	4,262.15
West Virginia	58	8,655	60.5	280,391	533.83	6.8	3,612.16
Wisconsin	130	19,041	63.1	649,634	523.00	6.8	3,528.52
Wyoming	27	2,175	52.9	51,506	432.43	8.2	3,496.68

*Reported by hospital as expense.
SOURCE: American Hospital Association. Hospital Statistics, 1989.

Table 4.10

Percent Change in Selected Components of Consumer Prices (Urban consumers) (1980–1990)

	1980	1981	1982	1983	1984	1985	1986	1987	1988	1989	1990
All items	**13.5**	**10.3**	**6.2**	**3.2**	**4.3**	**3.6**	**1.9**	**3.6**	**4.1**	**4.8**	**5.4**
Food/beverages	8.5	7.8	4.1	2.3	3.7	2.3	3.3	4.0	4.1	5.7	5.8
Housing	15.7	11.5	7.2	2.7	4.1	4.0	3.0	3.0	3.8	3.8	4.5
Apparel/upkeep	7.1	4.8	2.6	2.5	1.9	2.8	0.9	4.4	4.3	2.8	4.6
Transportation	11.0	10.7	11.6	8.8	6.2	6.3	7.5	6.6	6.5	5.0	5.6
Medical care	11.0	10.7	11.6	8.8	6.2	6.3	7.5	6.6	6.5	7.7	9.0
Medical care commodities	*	*	*	*	*	*	*	*	*	*	8.4
Medical care services	*	*	*	*	*	*	*	*	*	*	9.3
Professional services	*	*	*	*	*	*	*	*	*	*	6.6
Hospital and related	*	*	*	*	*	*	*	*	*	*	10.9
Entertainment	9.0	7.8	6.5	4.3	3.7	3.9	3.4	3.3	4.3	6.4	4.7
Other goods and services	9.1	9.8	10.3	11.0	6.7	6.1	6.0	5.8	6.3	7.8	7.7

*not available
SOURCE: U.S. Department of Labor, Monthly Labor Review.

Table 4.11

Comparison of Hospital Semiprivate Room Charges by State and Territory (1987–1990)

States and territories	January 1987	January 1988	Percent change 1987–1988	January 1989	January 1990	Percent change 1989–1990
Average United States	**$239**	**$255**	**6.7**	**$264**	**$297**	**12.5**
Alabama	176	187	6.2	187	210	12.3
Alaska	318	331	4.0	378	407	7.7
Arizona	233	251	7.9	256	300	17.2
Arkansas	155	159	2.7	161	170	5.6
California	328	361	9.9	391	453	15.9
Colorado	242	261	7.9	273	321	17.5
Connecticut	333	344	3.3	396	456	15.2
Delaware	305	325	6.6	350	385	10.0
District of Columbia	423	449	6.2	325	325	0.0
Florida	202	218	7.9	239	271	13.4
Georgia	152	162	6.6	180	198	10.0
Hawaii	242	257	6.4	317	348	9.8
Idaho	230	250	8.6	233	259	11.2
Illinois	265	276	3.9	275	300	9.1
Indiana	206	224	8.9	225	258	14.7
Iowa	193	202	4.8	210	221	5.2
Kansas	201	216	7.7	239	256	7.1
Kentucky	199	215	8.4	217	242	11.5
Louisiana	200	209	4.4	181	203	12.2
Maine	232	257	10.9	279	335	20.1
Maryland	213	232	8.6	233	266	14.2
Massachusetts	286	312	8.9	327	351	7.3
Michigan	180	294	5.0	313	337	7.7
Minnesota	223	244	9.1	244	282	15.6
Mississippi	125	141	12.8	142	167	17.6
Missouri	213	226	5.7	245	268	8.9
Montana	214	219	2.1	284	318	12.0
Nebraska	173	182	5.4	185	209	13.0
Nevada	223	224	0.2	239	251	5.0
New Hampshire	221	238	7.9	272	304	11.8
New Jersey	212	229	7.7	226	273	20.8
New Mexico	232	234	0.8	240	254	5.8
New York	254	266	4.5	301	339	12.6
North Carolina	157	174	11.3	185	220	18.9
North Dakota	184	195	6.0	213	230	7.9
Ohio	261	276	5.5	281	308	9.6
Oklahoma	178	188	5.2	205	220	7.3
Oregon	263	287	8.8	301	338	12.3
Pennsylvania	284	301	6.0	318	375	17.9
Puerto Rico	131	140	6.5	154	158	2.6
Rhode Island	244	275	12.6	296	342	15.5
South Carolina	145	160	9.8	199	212	6.5
South Dakota	175	182	4.1	187	209	11.8
Tennessee	162	173	6.7	172	183	5.8
Texas	183	199	8.4	202	223	10.4
Utah	234	242	3.5	328	353	7.6
Vermont	257	284	10.7	303	378	24.8
Virginia	181	195	7.7	194	220	13.4
Washington	268	281	4.7	298	334	12.1
West Virginia	181	196	8.5	213	223	4.7
Wisconsin	172	186	8.3	214	222	3.7
Wyoming	177	189	6.6	219	234	6.9

NOTES: Semiprivate room rates are rounded to nearest dollar. Percent change is based on room rates prior to rounding.

SOURCE: Health Insurance Association of America, Hospital Semiprivate Room Charges Survey, 1989.

Table 4.12

Median Physician Fees for Surgical Procedures by Specialty (1990)

Specialty	Fees	Specialty	Fees
General surgery		**Neurosurgery**	
Appendectomy	$ 810	Cranioplasty	$2,801
Cholecystectomy	1,288	Craniotomy	3,276
Inguinal hernia (unilateral)	801	Neuroplasty, median nerve	900
Modified radical mastectomy	1,500	Cervical discectomy (anterior)	3,000
Obstetrics/Gynecology		**Plastic surgery**	
Complete obstetrical care (usual or routine)	1,664	Complete rhinoplasty	2,500
Total hysterectomy	1,836	Facial rhytidectomy	3,000
Dilation and curettage (diagnostic)	486	Suction-assisted lipectomy, trunk	1,501
Dilation and curettage (therapeutic for		Dermabrasion of facial scar	500
abortion)	500	Excision of benign lesion	151
		Blepharoplasty, upper eyelids	1,338
Thoracic surgery		Breast reduction (bilateral)	3,720
Diagnostic flexible bronchoscopy	450		
Lobectomy	2,501	**Orthopedic surgery**	
Esophagoscopy (dilation)	446	Arthrocentesis of knee	55
Thoracentesis	151	Diagnostic knee arthroscopy	706
Abdominal aortic aneurysm repair	3,201	Knee arthroscopy with meniscectomy	1,601
		Closed reduction of Colles' fracture	451
		Total hip arthroplasty	3,522
		Total knee arthroplasty	3,501

SOURCE: Medical Economics, October 1, 1990. Copyright © 1990. Reprinted by permission.

Table 4.13

Median Physician Fees for Office Visits by Region and Specialty (1990)

Specialty	First office visits				Office revisits			
	West	Midwest	South	East	West	Midwest	South	East
Family practice	$111	$ 76	$ 75	*	$45	$33	$34	*
General practice	100	61	61	$ 61	40	31	32	$33
Internal medicine	137	91	98	101	48	40	40	48
Obstetrics/Gynecology	95	61	64	76	50	40	41	51
Pediatricians	81	46	49	55	42	33	33	40
General surgeons	*	65	64	76	*	35	40	41
Neurosurgeons	157	106	130	155	51	41	50	*
Orthopedic surgeons	124	83	91	100	51	41	40	50
Plastic surgeons	88	*	66	76	48	*	43	49
Thoracic surgeons	*	*	*	*	*	*	*	*
All surgical specialists	100	61	62	76	49	36	37	49
All nonsurgical specialists (except family practice and general practice)	131	90	95	100	47	40	40	50

*Data incomplete.

SOURCE: Medical Economics, October 1, 1990. Copyright © 1990. Reprinted by permission.

Table 4.14

Cost of Physician Office Visits by Specialty, Community, and Size of Practice Groups (1990)

Type of physician	First office visits			Office revisits		
	Urban	Suburban	Rural	Urban	Suburban	Rural
Cardiovascular surgeons	$105	—	—	$51	—	—
Family practitioners	83	$ 90	$70	36	$40	—
General practitioners	76	75	56	36	36	$30
General surgeons	75	76	66	37	41	40
Internists	113	106	90	44	43	36
Neurosurgeons	141	131	—	51	50	—
OBG specialists	76	75	64	48	47	39
Orthopedic surgeons	101	100	76	48	47	—
Otolaryngologist	70	70	—	40	41	—
Pediatricians	61	55	46	36	36	31
Plastic surgeons	76	71	—	43	43	—
Thoracic surgeons	93	—	—	41	—	—
All surgical specialists	80	75	61	43	43	35
All nonsurgical specialists	111	98	80	46	41	36

. . . and by size of group

Number of physicians in practice group	First office visit	Office revisits
3 MDs	$ 76	$41
4 MDs	86	40
5–9 MDs	90	41
10–24 MDs	95	41
25–49 MDs	101	45
50 MDs or more	119	49
MDs single-specialty group	81	41
MDs multi-specialty group	101	44

— = insufficient sample.

NOTE: MDs refers to any physician.

SOURCE: Medical Economics, October 1, 1990. Copyright © 1990. Reprinted by permission.

Table 4.15

Cost of Maternity Care, Physicians' Fees, and Hospital Charges by U.S. Census Region (1989) (Weighted averages)

	Normal delivery			Cesarean delivery		
	Total	Metropolitan	Nonmetropolitan	Total	Metropolitan	Nonmetropolitan
Total	**$4,334**	**$4,564**	**$4,128**	**$7,186**	**$7,633**	**$6,736**
Hospital charges	2,842	2,925	2,749	5,133	5,288	4,916
Physicians' fees	1,492	1,639	1,379	2,053	2,345	1,820

Regions

	Normal delivery	Cesarean delivery
Northeast		
Total	$4,456	$7,879
Hospital charges	2,964	5,826
Physicians' fees	1,492	2,053
Midwest		
Total	4,149	6,741
Hospital charges	2,657	4,688
Physicians' fees	1,492	2,053
South		
Total	4,204	7,087
Hospital charges	2,712	5,034
Physicians' fees	1,492	2,053
West		
Total	4,237	7,586
Hospital charges	2,745	5,533
Physicians' fees	1,492	2,053

NOTE: Physicians' fees include prenatal charges and delivery fees.

SOURCES: HIAA. The Cost of Maternity Care and Childbirth in the United States, 1989, and 1989 HIAA Surgical Prevailing Healthcare Charges System.

Table 4.16

Diagnosed Mental Disorders by Sex, Age, and Region (1989) (Thousands)

Mental disorders	Total	Male	Female	Under 15 years	15–44 years	45–64 years	65 years and over	Northeast	Midwest	South	West
Total mental disorders	**1,514**	**778**	**736**	**457**	**937**	**294**	**239**	**457**	**413**	**442**	**203**
Senile and presenile organic psychotic conditions	36	15	21	0	0	0	35	7	10	15	0
Alcohol psychoses	53	42	10	0	27	20	6	17	13	13	10
Drug psychoses	15	6	8	0	8	0	0	0	0	0	0
Transient organic psychotic conditions	24	10	15	0	6	0	14	6	6	10	0
Schizophrenia	204	120	84	0	145	47	11	87	49	44	24
Affective psychosis	372	128	244	9	204	85	75	120	98	106	48
Simple paranoia	9	0	6	0	0	0	0	0	0	0	0
Other nonorganic psychoses	55	24	32	0	21	14	20	16	14	17	8
Neurotic disorders	112	43	69	5	65	25	17	24	32	35	21
Personality disorders	25	11	14	0	21	0	0	13	6	0	0
Acute alcoholic intoxication	218	165	53	0	149	55	14	54	66	71	28
Opioid-type dependence	113	72	41	0	105	0	0	28	34	37	14
Depression disorders	34	10	24	0	23	0	5	7	11	13	0
All other	259	142	115	33	163	45	41	78	74	81	50

SOURCE: National Center for Health Statistics, Health Interview Survey, 1989.

Table 4.17

The 25 Most Frequently Performed Radiological and Imaging Procedures (Inpatient) (1990)

Procedure	Total performed	Payer			
		Private insurance	Medicare	Medicaid	Other
CT scan of head	1,399,280	360,692	759,363	105,717	173,510
Diagnostic ultrasound of heart	967,907	247,901	564,948	58,520	96,537
Routine chest X-ray	765,930	233,828	394,755	62,518	74,829
Upper gastrointestinal with barium	81,349	23,226	39,504	7,909	10,708
Lower gastrointestinal series	249,069	65,734	147,858	14,088	21,391
Chest X-ray	246,034	69,117	131,745	20,063	25,108
Pregnancy ultrasound	194,899	88,851	1,165	56,021	48,862
X-ray of urinary system	92,693	35,520	38,820	7,814	10,541
Lumbosacral spine X-ray	81,905	29,244	34,596	4,131	13,933
Isotope liver scan	148,709	47,618	74,992	11,547	14,553
Isotope bone scan	315,480	80,442	190,473	16,377	28,187

SOURCE: Healthcare Knowledge Systems.

Table 4.18

Surgical Procedure Utilization and Average Charge (Mutual of Omaha Insurance Company claimants only) (1988–1990)

	Inpatient surgeries						Outpatient surgeries					
	Number of surgeries per 1,000 people			Average charge per surgery			Number of surgeries per 1,000 people			Average charge per surgery		
State	1988	1989	1990	1988	1989	1990	1988	1989	1990	1988	1989	1990
United States	75	76	78	$ 919	$ 974	$1,012	52	58	63	$502	$530	$576
Alabama	94	87	88	833	964	1,003	69	67	72	475	556	516
Alaska	NA	42	68	NA	1,408	1,105	NA	50	42	NA	682	739
Arizona	59	82	75	1,176	1,109	1,191	56	66	69	620	657	710
Arkansas	76	85	78	758	908	787	54	65	61	421	486	538
California	61	66	70	1,226	1,283	1,246	37	46	62	753	764	754
Colorado	61	67	77	947	1,018	990	50	66	68	502	520	583
Connecticut	NA	NA	NA	NA	NA	NA	NA	NA	NA	NA	NA	NA
Delaware	68	53	62	882	1,110	1,068	56	48	47	444	512	533
District of Columbia	NA	NA	NA	NA	NA	NA	NA	NA	NA	NA	NA	NA
Florida	82	85	95	1,220	1,243	1,110	57	66	87	584	639	697
Georgia	79	99	94	1,045	1,046	1,167	43	51	58	626	574	635
Hawaii	NA	NA	NA	NA	NA	NA	NA	NA	NA	NA	NA	NA
Idaho	72	NA	NA	757	NA	NA	NA	NA	NA	NA	NA	NA
Illinois	87	82	78	1,076	1,130	1,033	63	65	67	537	569	589
Indiana	92	100	89	956	1,019	1,062	73	76	87	463	543	483
Iowa	58	52	61	735	859	830	44	45	54	397	414	477
Kansas	55	54	60	832	952	914	54	69	65	351	439	473
Kentucky	54	72	88	957	1,003	918	53	86	87	452	426	479
Louisiana	80	110	116	827	744	1,022	43	67	76	430	462	497
Maine	NA	NA	NA	NA	NA	NA	NA	NA	NA	NA	NA	NA
Maryland	74	65	78	1,070	1,424	1,266	44	64	65	683	543	579
Massachusetts	97	66	78	1,087	1,311	1,343	79	72	78	477	505	478
Michigan	69	55	55	726	935	830	69	79	79	470	473	435
Minnesota	66	73	71	804	902	934	46	45	45	464	441	506
Mississippi	91	102	128	761	828	748	55	55	62	476	461	447
Missouri	78	86	80	887	1,021	984	63	65	78	480	556	562
Montana	61	69	66	868	946	954	36	42	46	439	508	550
Nebraska	80	77	78	660	709	753	57	61	63	422	443	470
Nevada	55	65	60	993	1,198	1,337	NA	57	62	NA	621	732
New Hampshire	NA	NA	NA	NA	NA	NA	NA	NA	NA	NA	NA	NA
New Jersey	65	73	76	1,251	1,277	1,353	34	NA	47	547	NA	673
New Mexico	NA	49	NA	NA	910	NA	NA	NA	NA	NA	NA	NA
New York	62	64	70	1,736	1,682	1,926	30	32	34	823	708	869
North Carolina	54	64	56	928	880	828	43	40	44	569	519	609
North Dakota	NA	91	NA	NA	698	NA	NA	72	NA	NA	556	NA
Ohio	79	74	79	864	949	1,145	70	80	105	388	450	491
Oklahoma	78	74	54	921	926	1,045	84	75	74	433	370	384
Oregon	59	63	62	999	1,060	1,154	47	42	47	582	592	648
Pennsylvania	49	39	58	1,167	1,334	1,155	40	43	60	572	509	515
Rhode Island	NA	NA	NA	NA	NA	NA	NA	NA	NA	NA	NA	NA
South Carolina	NA	NA	NA	NA	NA	NA	NA	NA	NA	NA	NA	NA
South Dakota	62	79	66	768	805	803	35	51	42	354	494	534
Tennessee	95	99	109	779	836	930	53	69	77	424	503	495
Texas	108	102	110	957	1,056	1,106	63	70	78	563	618	703
Utah	74	58	70	890	839	886	69	78	82	515	453	578

Continued

Table 4.18 *(Continued)*

State	Inpatient surgeries						Outpatient surgeries					
	Number of surgeries per 1,000 people			Average charge per surgery			Number of surgeries per 1,000 people			Average charge per surgery		
	1988	1989	1990	1988	1989	1990	1988	1989	1990	1988	1989	1990
Vermont	NA	NA	NA	NA	NA	NA	NA	NA	NA	NA	NA	NA
Virginia	49	41	53	962	1,077	1,343	NA	52	52	NA	641	521
Washington	51	52	59	1,170	1,238	1,289	29	35	41	548	588	650
West Virginia	NA	91	NA	NA	796	NA	NA	NA	NA	NA	NA	NA
Wisconsin	57	72	61	730	835	822	40	48	40	411	375	506
Wyoming	NA	NA	66	NA	NA	813	NA	NA	NA	NA	NA	NA

SOURCE: Mutual of Omaha Insurance Company, Current Trends in Health Care Costs and Utilization.

Table 4.19

Cost of Accidents by Class (Billions)

	Total	Motor vehicle	Work	Home	Public nonmotor vehicle
Total costs	$143.4	$70.2	$47.1	$17.4	$10.9
Wage loss	37.1	20.3	7.9	5.8	4.7
Medical expense	23.6	5.0	8.1	6.7	4.4
Insurance administration	28.7	21.3	6.0	0.8	0.6
Fire loss	8.4	NA	3.1	4.1	1.2
Motor vehicle property damage	23.6	23.6	NA	NA	NA
Indirect work loss	22.0	NA	22.0	NA	NA

NOTES: Duplications between work and motor vehicle are eliminated in totals. Home and public insurance administration may include costs of administering medical treatment claims for some motor vehicle injuries through health plans.
SOURCE: National Safety Council, 1989.

Chapter 5

HEALTH SERVICES, RESOURCES, AND UTILIZATION

Community hospitals (defined as nonfederal, short-term, general, and special hospitals) provide acute care to the public. They account for 82 percent of all hospitals and 92 percent of all hospital admissions in the United States.

According to the 1990–91 edition of *Hospital Statistics*, published by the AHA, community hospital admissions dropped to 31.1 million in 1989 from 31.5 million in 1988. The average number of beds per community hospital remained at 171 in 1989, and admission rates dropped to 126.2 per 1,000 people. (Table 5.1) Hospitals reported 286 million outpatient visits in 1989, an increase of 6 percent over the previous year. This reflected a continuing trend toward the use of new facilities for the treatment of both medical and psychiatric patients on an outpatient basis. The 10 percent increase in outpatient visits reported in 1988 was the highest rate of growth in outpatient use in more than a decade.

The increasing use of ambulatory care as an alternative to hospitalization is evident in the proliferation of ambulatory care centers across the United States and the number of patient visits to these centers. In the United States, 81.7 percent of community hospitals now have organized outpatient service departments providing outpatient surgery, examination, diagnosis, and treatment of a variety of nonemergency medical conditions on an ambulatory basis.

Special geriatric services are offered at 2,937 community hospitals across the country. Hospice service, a concept of palliative care for the dying, is available at 804 hospitals and at an increasing number of freestanding facilities across the United States. To be eligible for reimbursement by Medicare, hospices must be certified by the U.S. Department of Health and Human Services.

◆ Utilization by Diagnosis

With the exception of obstetrical procedures for women, operations on the digestive system were the most common type of procedure performed on both sexes.

According to the NCHS, the most frequent diagnoses for patients under 15 years of age were infectious and parasitic diseases, pneumonia, and chronic disease of the tonsils and adenoids. Mental disorders, diseases of the genito-urinary system, fractures, and heart disease were the most frequent diagnoses of patients 15 to 44 years of age, excluding females with obstetrical deliveries. Patients 45 to 64 years of age were hospitalized most frequently for heart disease, and the most common diagnoses for those 65 years of age and more were heart disease and malignant neoplasms. (Table 5.3)

Women are operated on more frequently than men. In 1988, there were 23.5 million surgical procedures performed on women and 15.7 million on men. The majority of the surgical procedures were performed on people in the 15 to 44 age group. (Table 5.4)

Diagnosis-related groups. In 1975, HCFA contracted with Yale University to develop a patient classification system to support a hospital inpatient prospective payment system for Medicare. The fundamental principle involves paying all hospitals the same fixed sum to cover all costs associated with treating a patient falling within a specific diagnosis-related group (DRG). Hospitals that provide the necessary services efficiently realize a net gain while those that are inefficient will find the DRG payment does not cover their costs. This system developed by Yale was tested in the early 1980s and found to be a viable system for measuring hospital output and implementing a prospective payment system. As more data are collected and medical technology advances, DRGs are reviewed and revised as mandated by Congress.

Tables 5.11 and 5.12 list the 10 most frequent medical diagnoses and the 10 most frequent procedures performed by hospitals in the United States.

◆ Physician Contacts

Collectively, people in the United States contacted their physicians either in person or by telephone more than 1.3 billion times during 1989. Women made more visits to both their doctors' offices (461 million) and hospitals (92 million) than men did, contacting physicians an average of 6.1 times each in 1989. Men contacted physicians, as women did, primarily at physician offices (319 million times), but averaged only 4.7 times each during 1989.

Americans of all ages, races, and economic groups contacted their physicians more times during 1989, averaging 8.2 times in the 65–74 age group, and 9.9 times for those 75 years and more.

In 1989, community hospitals continued to add additional patient services and additional special facilities such as genetic counseling, rehabilitation, and occupational therapy departments. (Table 5.6)

The average length of a hospital stay in the United States in 1986 was shorter for most illnesses and surgical procedures than in any other country in the world. (Table 5.7)

◆ Hospital Facilities and Numbers of Physicians

The number of community hospitals, many in rural areas, has been declining since 1978. Since 1980, 440 community hospitals have ceased to provide inpatient acute care services. In 1989, there were 5,455 community hospitals in operation.

The decrease in the number of hospitals was accompanied by a decline of 1.5 percent in the number of hospital beds, from 947,000 in 1988 to 933,000 in 1989. (Table 5.9)

The occupancy rate in community hospitals was approximately 65 percent between 1988 and 1989 and the average length of stay remained at 7.2 days.

Although fewer beds are available, the scope of services has increased with advances in medical technology. Hospitals today offer more types of procedures and treatments to patients on an outpatient basis. Occupancy in community hospitals continues to decrease partly because of expanded outpatient and ambulatory services.

Occupancy rates in private psychiatric hospitals remained at a steady 67 percent in the two-year period between 1988 and 1990. The overall length of stay dropped 16 percent to 26.1 days according to the National Association of Private Psychiatric Hospitals. Nearly half of the patients in these hospitals were diagnosed with affective disorders, including depression and manic depressive illness.

HCFA estimates the number of practicing physicians will increase from about 588,000 in 1990 to nearly 697,000 in 2000, an increase of almost 19 percent. (Table 5.8)

◆ Organ Transplants

Organ transplants were performed clinically first in 1953. The number and success of these life-saving procedures grew dramatically as a result of the improvements in surgical techniques and the introduction in 1983 of the immunosuppressive drug cyclosporine. In 1990 there were 15,164 organ transplants and more than 500,000 tissue transplants of various types in the United States.

Kidney transplants composed the majority (9,560) of the 15,164 organ transplants performed at 242 transplant centers in the United States in 1990.

It is estimated that 2,206 of the 22,008 patients awaiting organ transplants died in 1990 due to the scarcity of transplantable organs. (See Table 5.10.)

Table 5.1

Community Hospital Statistics (1950–1989)

Year	Beds per 1,000 population	Occupancy rates (percent)	Average number of persons hospitalized per day per 1,000 population	Admissions per 1,000 population	Average length of stay (days)
1950	3.4	NA	2.5	111.4	8.1
1955	3.5	NA	2.5	117.3	7.8
1960	3.6	NA	2.7	129.2	7.6
1965	3.9	NA	3.0	138.8	7.8
1970	4.2	NA	3.3	145.6	8.2
1975	4.5	75.0	3.3	158.1	7.7
1980	4.4	75.6	3.3	162.1	7.6
1981	4.5	76.0	3.4	161.9	7.6
1982	4.5	75.3	3.4	160.2	7.6
1983	4.4	73.5	3.3	157.6	7.6
1984	4.4	69.0	3.0	151.8	7.3
1985	4.3	64.8	2.8	143.1	7.1
1986	4.1	64.3	2.7	137.0	7.1
1987	4.0	64.9	2.6	132.4	7.2
1988	3.9	65.5	2.5	128.9	7.2
1989	3.8	66.2	2.5	126.2	7.2

SOURCE: American Hospital Association, Hospital Statistics, various annual editions.

Table 5.2

Patients Discharged from Short-Stay Hospitals, Days of Care, and Average Lengths of Stay by Sex, Age, Race, and Income (1989)

	Hospital discharges		Hospital days	
	Number per 100 persons	Number in thousands	Average length of stay	Number in thousands
All persons	11.3	27,423	6.5	179,332
Age				
Under 5 years	7.7	1,438	6.6	9,501
5–17 years	3.4	1,531	5.6	8,561
18–24 years	11.5	2,926	4.1	121
25–44 years	9.8	7,746	4.8	37,022
45–64 years	13.1	6,020	7.2	43,233
65–74 years	23.7	4,219	8.5	34,733
75 years and more	31.1	3,543	9.4	33,246
Sex and age				
Male				
All ages	9.6	11,298	7.3	82,595
Under 18 years	4.7	1,543	6.0	9,200
18–44 years	6.0	3,044	5.8	17,526
45–64 years	13.9	3,076	7.2	22,284
65 years and more	29.9	3,635	9.2	33,585
Female				
All ages	12.8	16,125	6.0	96,737
Under 18 years	4.6	1,426	6.2	8,862
18–44 years	14.4	7,628	4.1	31,531
45–64 years	12.2	2,944	7.1	20,949
65 years and more	24.2	4,127	8.6	35,394
Race and age				
White				
All ages	11.4	23,311	6.5	152,323
Under 18 years	4.7	2,403	6.3	15,091
18–44 years	40.2	8,882	4.6	40,499
45–64 years	12.9	5,154	7.1	36,669
65 years and more	26.1	6,873	8.7	60,065
Black				
All ages	11.5	3,442	6.8	23,260
Under 18 years	5.1	504	5.5	2,795
18–44 years	11.5	1,468	5.0	7,294
45–64 years	15.2	715	8.2	5,841
65 years and more	30.8	755	9.7	7,329

Continued

Table 5.2 *(Continued)*

Family income and age	Hospital discharges		Hospital days	
	Number per 100 persons	Number in thousands	Average length of stay	Number in thousands
Under $10,000				
All ages	18.0	4,704	7.3	34,432
Under 18 years	7.4	550	6.0	3,273
18–44 years	16.9	1,654	4.8	7,958
45–64 years	24.2	814	9.5	7,767
65 years and more	30.0	1,686	9.2	15,434
$10,000–$19,999				
All ages	13.7	5,641	6.9	38,672
Under 18 years	4.7	504	6.3	3,154
18–44 years	12.4	1,967	4.6	8,951
45–64 years	15.6	1,011	6.9	6,944
65 years and more	27.0	2,158	9.1	19,624
$20,000–$34,000				
All ages	10.3	5,848	6.2	35,966
Under 18 years	4.3	679	6.6	4,461
18–44 years	10.4	2,700	4.6	12,548
45–64 years	13.3	1,313	6.3	8,242
65 years and more	22.1	1,156	9.3	10,715
$35,000 and more				
All ages	7.8	6,264	5.7	355,686
Under 18 years	3.9	829	6.6	5,430
18–44 years	7.8	2,910	4.5	13,150
45–64 years	9.8	1,756	5.8	10,242
65 years and more	22.1	769	8.9	6,864

SOURCE: National Center for Health Statistics.

Table 5.3

Patients Discharged from Short-Stay Hospitals by Category of First-Listed Diagnosis, Sex, and Age (1988) (Thousands)

First-listed diagnostic category	Total	Sex		Age			
		Male	Female	Under 15 years	15–44 years	45–64 years	65 years or more
All conditions	**31,146**	**12,642**	**18,504**	**2,610**	**11,934**	**6,456**	**10,146**
Heart disease	3,641	1,955	1,686	14	243	1,162	2,223
Malignant neoplasms and carcinoma-in-situ	1,670	772	898	37	187	566	880
Benign neoplasms and neoplasms of uncertain behavior	428	78	350	16	191	142	79
Fractures, all sites	1,014	506	508	107	356	154	398
Diseases of the genito-urinary system	2,204	828	1,376	71	922	512	700
Pneumonia, all forms	924	472	452	184	111	139	490
Chronic disease of tonsils and adenoids	197	87	110	125	70	—	—
Cerebrovascular disease	784	336	448	—	32	171	578
Diabetes mellitus	454	209	245	28	125	134	166
Inguinal hernia	257	232	25	30	65	78	84
Cholelithiasis	484	132	352	—	183	146	154
Appendicitis	242	141	101	52	145	24	20
Mental disorders	1,559	765	793	58	962	288	251
Infectious and parasitic diseases	693	333	359	191	211	104	187
Hyperplasia of the prostate	247	247	—	—	—	56	191
Females with obstetrical deliveries	3,781	—	3,781	10	3,768	—	—

SOURCE: National Center for Health Statistics, Advancedata, 1989.

Table 5.4

Procedures Provided to Patients Discharged from Short-Stay Hospitals by Sex and Age (1988) (Thousands)

Procedure	Sex			Age			
	Total	Male	Female	Under 15 years	15–44 years	45–64 years	65 years or more
All procedures	39,192	15,735	23,457	2,050	15,520	8,939	12,682
Operations on the nervous system	896	467	429	216	279	200	201
Operations on the endocrine system	111	31	79	—	43	39	26
Operations on the eye	547	243	304	33	80	126	308
Operations on the ear	198	109	88	107	46	25	19
Operations on the nose, mouth, and pharynx	820	436	385	220	372	135	94
Operations on the respiratory system	991	561	430	69	190	291	441
Operations on the cardiovascular system	3,626	2,220	1,406	169	422	1,358	1,676
Operations on the hemic and lymphatic systems	392	192	200	24	91	106	172
Operations on the digestive system	5,257	2,277	2,981	233	1,244	1,335	2,145
Operations on the urinary system	1,706	1,018	688	48	398	426	833
Operations on the male genital organs	633	633	—	50	54	128	400
Operations on the female genital organs	2,501	—	2,501	10	1,773	516	202
Obstetrical procedures	6,042	—	6,042	16	6,024	—	—
Operations on the musculoskeletal system	3,143	1,648	1,496	203	1,325	747	868
Operations on the integumentary system	1,475	639	836	105	537	393	440
Miscellaneous diagnostic and therapeutic procedures	10,854	5,262	5,593	544	2,342	3,112	4,856

NOTE: Details may not add to total due to rounding.
SOURCE: National Center for Health Statistics. Advancedata, 1989.

Table 5.5

Number of Physician Contacts Per Person Per Year by Place of Contact, Age, Sex, and Race (1989)

Characteristic	All places	Telephone	Office	Hospital	Other	All places	Telephone	Office	Hospital	Other
	Number per person per year					Number in thousands				
All persons	5.4	0.6	3.2	0.7	0.8	1,322,890	155,431	780,153	175,067	203,433
Age										
Under 5 Years	6.7	1.0	4.1	0.7	0.9	126,309	19,441	76,992	12,248	16,685
5–17 years	3.5	0.4	2.2	0.5	0.4	157,698	19,356	99,007	20,420	17,967
18–24 years	3.9	0.4	2.1	0.6	0.8	98,233	10,685	52,641	15,102	19,426
25–44 years	5.1	0.6	3.0	0.7	0.8	398,368	46,735	232,550	52,719	64,030
45–64 years	6.1	0.8	3.6	0.9	0.9	283,351	350,032	165,682	40,399	39,602
65–74 years	8.2	0.8	4.8	1.3	1.3	145,949	14,467	84,725	22,527	23,368
75 years and more	9.9	0.9	6.0	1.0	2.0	112,982	9,715	68,557	11,652	22,355
Sex and age										
Male										
All ages	4.7	0.5	2.7	0.7	0.7	551,771	60,657	318,509	82,856	8,622
Under 18 years	4.7	0.7	2.9	0.5	0.6	155,533	22,241	95,454	17,939	18,747
18–44 years	3.4	0.3	1.8	0.6	0.6	171,895	15,440	93,576	29,334	32,583
45–64 years	5.2	0.6	3.1	0.8	0.8	115,404	12,616	67,441	17,876	16,679
65 years and more	9.0	0.9	5.1	1.5	1.5	108,940	10,361	62,039	17,708	18,211
Female										
All ages	6.1	0.8	3.7	0.7	0.9	771,119	94,773	461,644	92,211	117,213
Under 18 years	4.1	0.5	2.6	0.5	0.5	128,474	16,556	80,545	14,730	15,905
18–44 years	6.1	0.8	3.6	0.7	1.0	324,706	41,980	191,645	38,487	50,876
45–64 years	7.0	0.9	4.1	0.9	1.0	167,948	22,417	98,241	22,523	22,924
65 years and more	8.8	0.8	5.3	1.0	1.6	149,991	13,821	91,243	16,470	27,512
Race and age										
White										
All ages	5.6	0.7	3.4	0.7	0.8	1,148,076	140,796	690,961	141,195	167,771
Under 18 years	4.7	0.7	3.0	0.5	0.5	243,768	35,070	154,836	25,454	26,885
18–44 years	4.9	0.6	2.9	0.6	0.8	49,272	51,847	250,836	53,895	70,557
45–64 years	6.2	0.8	3.7	0.8	0.8	246,864	31,637	146,865	33,154	32,902
65 years and more	8.7	0.8	5.3	1.1	1.4	228,172	22,243	138,424	28,692	37,427
Black										
All ages	4.7	0.4	2.3	0.9	1.0	140,144	12,369	69,624	27,982	28,834
Under 18 years	3.1	0.3	1.6	0.6	0.6	31,194	2,935	16,035	6,130	5,815
18–44 years	4.1	0.4	2.0	0.9	0.8	52,553	4,691	25,856	11,309	10,122
45–64 years	6.3	0.6	3.3	1.2	1.1	29,512	2,931	15,430	5,797	5,024
65 years and more	11.0	0.7	5.0	1.9	3.2	26,885	1,812	12,304	4,716	7,873
Family income and age										
All ages	6.8	0.7	3.4	1.2	1.5	178,684	17,376	88,911	31,401	39,899
Under 18 years	4.5	0.4	2.3	0.9	0.8	33,348	3,019	17,004	6,982	5,979

Continued

Table 5.5 *(Continued)*

Characteristic	All places	Telephone	Office	Hospital	Other	All places	Telephone	Office	Hospital	Other
	Number per person per year					Number in thousands				
18–44 years	5.9	0.6	2.6	1.0	1.7	87,360	5,501	25,423	10,103	16,140
45–64 years	8.4	0.9	4.0	1.9	1.5	28,371	3,181	13,492	6,473	4,948
65 years and more	10.6	1.0	5.9	1.4	2.3	59,605	5,672	32,993	7,842	12,832
$10,000–$19,999										
All ages	5.8	0.7	3.2	0.8	1.1	239,204	26,978	131,868	33,651	45,378
Under 18 years	4.0	0.6	2.1	0.6	0.7	42,348	6,148	22,848	6,130	7,002
18–44 years	5.1	0.6	2.5	0.7	1.1	80,806	10,148	40,457	11,934	17,743
45–64 years	7.3	0.7	4.0	1.2	1.3	47,303	4,814	26,240	7,538	8,468
65 years and more	8.6	0.7	5.3	1.0	1.5	68,747	5,868	42,293	8,048	12,165
$20,000–34,999										
All ages	5.3	0.7	3.2	0.7	0.7	302,987	37,628	182,743	39,920	41,823
Under 18 years	4.4	0.6	2.9	0.5	0.4	69,329	9,630	44,976	7,371	6,913
18–44 years	5.1	0.6	3.0	0.7	0.8	132,002	15,349	77,447	19,110	19,933
45–64 years	6.0	0.8	3.7	0.8	0.8	59,544	7,486	36,137	7,977	7,817
65 years and more	8.0	1.0	4.6	1.0	1.4	42,112	5,162	24,188	5,462	7,158
$35,000 or more										
All ages	5.2	0.7	3.3	0.6	0.6	420,121	54,936	262,000	47,580	51,935
Under 18 years	5.1	0.7	3.4	0.4	0.5	109,814	15,880	72,532	9,662	11,050
18–44 years	4.5	0.6	2.8	0.5	0.6	169,045	20,776	106,178	19,760	21,106
45–64 years	6.0	0.8	3.5	0.7	0.8	106,660	14,720	63,482	12,761	14,191
65 years and more	9.9	1.0	5.7	1.5	1.6	34,601	3,561	19,803	5,396	5,587
Geographic region										
Northeast	5.4	0.6	3.2	0.9	0.7	262,920	31,007	155,154	43,017	32,118
Midwest	5.4	0.7	3.4	0.7	0.9	322,967	41,070	186,781	43,092	53,184
South	5.4	0.6	3.4	0.6	0.8	453,069	52,318	280,119	49,055	68,586
West	5.5	0.6	3.1	0.8	1.0	283,934	31,036	161,099	39,903	49,545

SOURCE: National Center for Health Statistics, Health Interview Survey, 1989.

Table 5.6

Percent of Community Hospitals with Selected Special Facilities, Services, and Special Beds (1980 –1989)

Facility	1980	1982	1984	1986	1988	1989
Emergency department	82	94	86	95	95	94
Rehabilitation (outpatient)	25	33	36	6	41	49
Family planning	20	11	12	29	32	39
Open-heart facility	22	11	11	13	14	16
X-ray therapy	21	20	17	18	18	19
Megavolt therapy	16	17	15	18	18	19
Radioactive implants	26	23	21	24	24	24
Organ transplantation	NA	4	NA	5	6	10
Blood bank	79	72	67	73	71	38
Respiratory therapy	94	91	85	93	92	91
Speech pathology	43	37	44	50	47	45
Hemodialysis (inpatient)	24	23	24	28	27	26
Genetic counseling	7	7	8	8	8	9
Physical therapy	88	88	87	91	88	85
Occupational therapy	33	36	45	46	45	48
Psychiatric partial hospital	12	10	14	12	17	13
Psychiatric (outpatient)	17	14	21	17	17	19
Alcohol-chemical dependency	15	12	18	18	19	20
Home care department	12	13	21	35	35	35
Hospice	6	9	10	15	15	16
CT scanners	23	31	42	60	60	67
Magnetic resonance imaging	NA	NA	NA	10	9	15
Birthing room	NA	NA	NA	NA	NA	65
Reproductive health services	NA	NA	NA	NA	NA	39

SOURCE: American Hospital Association, Hospital Statistics, 1990–1991.

Table 5.7

Length of Stay in Selected Countries for Selected Disease Categories (Days)

International Classification of Disease categories	United States	United Kingdom	Canada	France	Switzerland
Pulmonary tuberculosis	13.9	19.6	32.6	20.3	32.5
Malignant neoplasm of trachea, bronchus, and lung	8.8	11.4	17.8	13.8	16.1
Breast cancer	7.1	12.0	14.5	7.0	19.3
Prostate cancer	7.2	13.0	17.0	12.7	18.4
Diabetes mellitus	7.6	17.9	17.2	12.6	25.6
Alcoholic psychoses	NA	NA	19.4	17.0	19.6
Alcohol dependence syndrome	10.7	8.6	11.4	12.3	13.6
Inflammatory diseases of the eye	3.9	5.7	4.3	7.0	11.1
Cataract	1.7	6.4	4.0	8.4	11.1
Otitis	2.6	7.7	3.1	5.2	6.4
Rheumatic fever	9.1	11.8	13.3	12.6	16.3
Hypertension	5.6	13.5	13.5	10.2	19.6
Acute myocardial infarction	8.9	11.2	14.7	12.8	17.8
Pneumonia	7.8	39.9	16.8	13.4	16.9
Pneumococcal pneumonia	7.7	15.7	11.4	14.5	17.9
Bronchitis	3.6	15.8	8.7	13.2	18.7
Asthma	4.8	4.9	5.5	8.3	14.4
Ulcers of stomach/small intestine	7.1	10.7	10.5	13.1	14.1
Appendicitis	4.8	5.6	5.5	7.6	8.5
Hernia of abdominal cavity	3.0	5.5	5.5	6.0	NA
Cholelithiasis	6.9	9.9	9.2	11.5	14.2
Nephritis	11.0	11.7	13.1	11.0	17.6
Calculus of kidney and ureter	3.6	7.4	6.0	7.1	7.3
Cystitis	6.0	3.8	6.9	8.2	10.4
Normal delivery	2.4	4.3	4.2	6.3	8.5
Major puerperal infection	4.3	4.4	4.9	9.3	6.8
Infections of the skin	7.3	8.1	7.2	5.2	10.1
Other inflammatory diseases of skin	6.7	9.4	12.0	13.9	15.2
Osteoarthrosis	10.2	25.7	19.9	17.5	22.2
Intervertebral disc disorders	6.9	12.0	9.7	11.2	17.9
Respiratory distress syndrome	23.6	19.7	18.5	19.2	11.5
Hemolytic diseases and jaundice	7.0	6.7	3.7	7.4	7.4
Fracture of neck of femur	14.2	29.7	32.9	18.9	33.6
Sprains and strains of back	5.6	5.9	5.7	9.8	9.4

NOTES: Most current data for United States, France, and Switzerland are from 1986. United Kingdom and Canadian data are from 1985.

SOURCE: Organization for Economic Cooperation and Development.

Table 5.8

Estimates and Projections of Physicians and Dentists (1950–2000) (Thousands)

Year	Total U.S. population (millions)	Physicians			Dentists
		Total	Medical doctors	Osteopaths	
Actual					
1950	152.3	219.9	209.0	10.9	79.2
1955	165.9	240.2	228.6	11.6	84.4
1960	180.7	259.5	247.3	12.2	90.1
1965	194.3	288.7	277.6	11.1	96.0
1970	205.1	326.2	314.2	12.0	102.2
1975	215.9	384.4	370.4	14.0	112.0
1980	227.8	457.5	440.4	17.1	126.2
1981	230.1	466.7	448.7	18.0	129.2
1982	232.5	483.7	465.0	18.7	132.0
1983	234.8	501.2	481.5	19.7	135.1
1984	237.0	506.5	485.7	20.8	138.0
1985	239.3	520.7	498.8	21.9	140.8
1986	241.7	534.8	511.6	23.2	143.2
1987	243.9	548.5	524.1	24.4	145.5
1988	246.3	562.0	536.3	25.7	147.4
Projections					
1990	248.7	587.7	559.5	28.2	150.8
1995	255.2	645.5	611.1	34.4	156.8
2000	259.6	696.5	656.1	40.0	161.2

SOURCE: U.S. Department of Health and Human Services, Health Care Financing Administration.

Table 5.9

Community Hospitals, Beds, Admissions, and Occupancy (1972–1989)

Year	Hospitals	Beds (thousands)	Admissions (thousands)	Occupancy (percent)
1972	5,746	879	30,709	75.4
1973	5,789	898	31,671	75.7
1974	5,875	926	32,866	75.6
1975	5,875	942	33,435	75.0
1976	5,857	956	33,979	74.6
1977	5,881	969	34,273	73.8
1978	5,851	975	34,506	73.6
1979	5,842	984	35,098	73.9
1980	5,830	988	36,143	75.6
1981	5,813	1,003	36,438	76.0
1982	5,801	1,012	36,379	75.3
1983	5,783	1,018	36,152	73.5
1984	5,759	1,017	35,155	69.0
1985	5,732	1,001	33,449	64.8
1986	5,678	978	32,379	64.3
1987	5,611	958	31,604	64.9
1988	5,533	947	31,453	65.5
1989	5,455	933	31,116	66.2

SOURCE: American Hospital Association. Hospital Statistics, 1990–1991.

Table 5.10

Organ Transplants (1985–1990) and People Awaiting Organ Transplants in May 1991

Procedure	1985	1986	1987	1988	1989	1990	May 1991 awaiting transplant
Heart	719	1,368	1,438	1,633	1,700	2,085	2,045
Heart-Lung	30	45	49	74	68	50	586
Kidney	7,695	8,976	9,094	9,004	8,706	9,560	18,464
Liver	602	924	1,199	1,711	2,164	2,656	1,466
Lung	0	0	0	33	119	265	450
Pancreas	30	140	42	250	419	549	170
Total	**9,176**	**11,453**	**11,922**	**12,735**	**13,176**	**15,164**	**23,181**

SOURCE: United Network for Organ Sharing.

Table 5.11

The 10 Most Frequent Medical Diagnoses by DRG Code, Rank, Sex, and Average Cost (1990)

DRG	Number of diagnoses	Rank	Diagnosis	Sex (percent)		Average cost of diagnosis
				Male	Female	
391	176,863	1	Normal newborn	51.0	49.0	$ 457
373	153,362	2	Vaginal delivery with complications	0.0	100.0	1,252
243	50,558	3	Medical back problems	48.3	51.7	1,825
371	48,427	4	Cesarean section without complications and/or morbidity	0.0	100.0	2,674
127	46,347	5	Heart failure and shock	43.7	56.3	3,459
140	41,106	6	Angina pectoris	45.7	54.3	2,401
182	37,556	7	Esophagitis, gastroenteritis, and miscellaneous digestive disorders, age>70 and/or complications and/or morbidity	34.6	65.4	2,035
89	36,632	8	Simple pneumonia and pleurisy, age>70 and/ or complications and/or morbidity	49.2	50.8	3,929
430	34,143	9	Psychoses	40.0	60.0	3,385
355	31,284	10	Nonradical hysterectomy, age<70 without complications and/or morbidity	0.0	100.0	3,279

SOURCE: Agency for Health Care Policy and Research, Hospital Studies Program.

Table 5.12

The 10 Most Frequent Medical Procedures by DRG Code, Rank, Sex, and Average Cost (1990)

DRG	Number of procedures	Rank	Procedure	Sex (percent)		Average cost of DRG code
				Male	Female	
64.0	79,971	1	Circumcision	100.0	0.0	$ 451
73.6	67,090	2	Episiotomy	0.0	100.0	1,281
74.1	57,047	3	Low cervical Cesarean section	0.0	100.0	2,735
88.7	56,710	4	Diagnostic ultrasound	34.3	65.7	2,659
87.0	46,154	5	Soft tissue X-ray of face, head, and neck	45.1	54.9	2,962
73.5	42,267	6	Manually assisted delivery	0.0	100.0	1,263
37.2	37,616	7	Diagnostic procedures on heart and pericardium	62.5	37.5	2,890
51.2	31,701	8	Cholecystectomy	27.9	72.1	4,114
68.4	29,875	9	Total abdominal hysterectomy	0.0	100.0	3,501
89.5	29,684	10	Cardiac function tests	46.9	53.1	2,560

SOURCE: Agency for Health Care Policy and Research, Hospital Studies Program.

Chapter 6

DISABILITY, MORBIDITY, AND MORTALITY

◆ Disability

Disability income insurance is a form of health insurance provided by group and individual policies and by specific government programs to replace income for insured persons who become disabled and are unable to work because of illness, injury, or disease. Disability rates for both acute and chronic health conditions, as measured by work-loss days, restricted activity days, and disability days, vary by social and economic characteristics.

Occupational Illnesses and Injuries

The Bureau of Labor Statistics annual survey of occupational injuries and illnesses reported that in 1989 there were approximately 6.6 million job-related injuries and illnesses occurring at a rate of 8.6 per 100 full-time private sector workers, unchanged from the 1988 rate. (See graph.) Even though the rate was the same as in 1988, the number of cases increased by 136,000, occurring primarily in the trade and services industries.

Manufacturing led all industries with the highest injury and illness incidence rate in 1989, due to repeated motion, pressure, or vibration such as carpal tunnel syndrome.

Repeated traumas constituted 52 percent of the illness cases in 1989, while skin diseases accounted for 22 percent of the total.

Approximately 284,000 more job-related injuries were reported in the private sector in 1989 than in 1988, with manufacturing accounting for slightly more than 70 percent or 204,500 of the total illness cases reported and for nearly all the increase in illnesses in 1989. The rate in the manufacturing industry rose from 13.0 per 100 full-time workers in 1988 to 13.1 in 1989.

The probability of a male becoming temporarily or permanently disabled between the ages of 20 and 30 is 1.3 percent, but between the ages of 20 and 60 this increases to 19.1 percent. (Table 6.1) Females are less prone to disability during their lifetimes and have only a 15.3 percent chance of becoming dis-

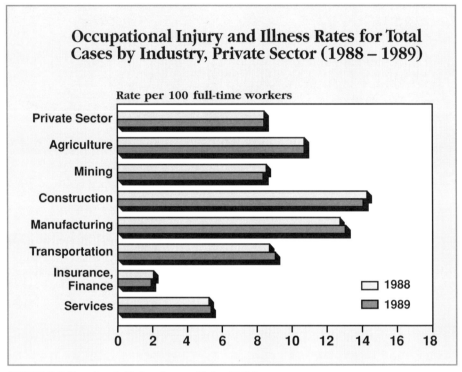

Occupational Injury and Illness Rates for Total Cases by Industry, Private Sector (1988 – 1989)

Rate per 100 full-time workers

SOURCE: U.S. Department of Labor, Bureau of Labor Statistics.

abled between 20 and 60 years of age. Data are based on males and females who turned 20 years old in 1986.

Table 6.2 shows that workers with higher incomes have fewer days of disability from acute health conditions. Males and females also have marked differences in the number of disability days. Females averaged 9.8 days and males averaged 6.9 days of restricted activity per person in 1988.

Acute Conditions

Some 358 million workdays were lost as a result of all acute health conditions in 1988, a 3 percent increase over 1987. Each worker in the metropolitan statistical area averaged 3.1 days off the job (Table 6.3). Men were more often unable to work due to injuries, and women lost more workdays due to respiratory infections.

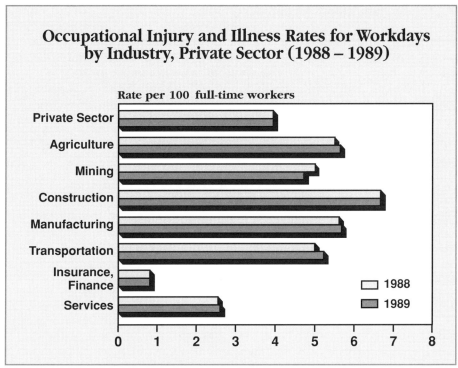

Occupational Injury and Illness Rates for Workdays by Industry, Private Sector (1988 – 1989)

SOURCE: U.S. Department of Labor, Bureau of Labor Statistics.

Chronic Conditions

In 1989, almost 35 million people, 14 percent of the U.S. civilian noninstitutionalized population (244.9 million), suffered some activity limitation because of one or more chronic conditions. Chronic conditions refer to long-term chronic disease or impairment. These chronic conditions and long-term latent illnesses often are difficult to recognize and are often not recorded accurately.

◆ Social Security Disability Insurance Program

The Social Security Disability Insurance Program is the largest federal income program for disabled persons. Table 6.6 shows the growth of this program from 1965 to 1989.

The number of workers and dependents receiving benefits through Social Security increased from 2.8 million in 1988 to 2.9 million people in 1989. There were 4.1 million disabled workers and dependents who received a total of $22.9 billion in benefits through the program in 1989.

◆ Morbidity and Mortality

Despite medical breakthroughs and environmental changes, cardiovascular-renal diseases and cancer are still the leading causes of death in the United States. Deaths from cancer increased slightly from 198.6 per 100,000 population to 200.3 in 1989, while deaths from heart disease, pneumonia, tuberculosis, and cerebrovascular diseases continued to decrease, as they have since 1960.

Life expectancy at birth remained the same as it was in 1988, 71.5 years for males, 78.3 years for females. (Table 6.7)

The death rate in the United States has been affected in the past few years by acquired immune deficiency syndrome (AIDS). NCHS reported in the January 1991 Monthly Vital Statistics Report that human immunodeficiency virus infection (HIV infection) ranked 15th in 1988, but has now become the 11th leading cause of death in the United States. In 1990, the Centers for Disease Control in Atlanta reported 33,705 new cases and 24,134 deaths. (Table 6.8) It is estimated by CDC that 1.5 million Americans are infected with the AIDS virus.

AIDS is the second-leading cause of death among men aged 25 to 44, surpassing heart disease, cancer, suicide, and homicide and is now becoming a leading killer of young women. In 1989, HIV infection/AIDS ranked eighth among causes of death among women aged 24 to 44 and if trends continue, it will become one of the five leading causes of death in that group.

Although the overall crude death rate in the United States has decreased generally over the years, it remained the same (8.7 per 1,000 population) in 1989 as it was in 1988.

The downward trend in the mortality rate is in part the result of a decline in the incidence of heart and cardiovascular disease. Mortality rates for these two causes decreased 7.4 percent from 1982 to 1989.

Table 6.1

Probability of Disability Between Age 20 and Attained Age for Workers Eligible for Social Security Income (1986)

From age 20 to age	Probability of insured disability from age 20 (percent)	
	Males	Females
21	0.1	0.0
25	0.5	0.3
30	1.3	0.7
35	2.3	1.5
40	3.5	2.6
45	5.2	4.1
50	7.8	6.4
55	12.0	9.9
60	19.1	15.3
65	29.2	22.1
66	30.8	23.1
67	32.2	24.0

SOURCE: U.S. Department of Health and Human Services, Social Security Administration.

Table 6.2

Disability Days Due to Acute Conditions by Social and Economic Characteristics (1987–1988)

	Restricted activity			Bed disability			Work-loss 18 years or more		
	1987	1988	1989	1987	1988	1989	1987	1988	1989
Sex									
Male	6.1	6.9	6.6	2.5	2.4	2.9	2.8	2.7	3.0
Female	7.7	9.8	8.3	3.4	3.5	3.9	3.4	2.7	3.9
Family income									
Under $10,000	9.1	10.0	10.6	4.4	4.7	4.9	4.1	3.8	5.1
$10,000–19,999	7.3	7.7	8.1	3.3	3.4	3.8	NA	NA	NA
$20,000–34,999	6.8	6.5	7.6	2.8	2.7	3.4	NA	NA	NA
$35,000 and more	5.8	5.8	6.0	2.4	2.4	2.7	2.4	NA	NA
Place of residence									
Metropolitan	6.7	6.8	7.4	3.1	3.0	3.4	3.1	3.1	3.1
Other	7.1	7.3	7.7	3.0	3.0	3.5	3.0	3.1	3.4
Age									
Under 5 years	9.4	9.7	9.6	4.4	4.9	4.5	NA	NA	NA
5–17 years	6.5	7.2	7.9	2.9	3.4	4.1	NA	NA	NA
18–24 years	6.9	7.1	7.5	3.0	3.0	3.2	3.4	3.5	3.9
25–44 years	6.3	6.4	7.1	2.7	2.5	3.0	3.1	3.2	3.6
45–66 years	6.1	5.8	5.9	2.6	2.4	2.8	2.9	2.5	2.5
65 years and more	8.1	8.1	9.9	3.4	3.4	4.2	NA	NA	NA

NOTES: The data refer to the civilian, noninstitutionalized population. A restricted activity day is one on which a person cuts down on his or her usual activities for the whole day because of illness or injury. A bed disability day is one on which a person stays in bed for all or most of the day because of a specific illness or injury. Family income includes the total income of each member of the family.

SOURCE: U.S. Department of Health and Human Services, National Center for Health Statistics, Current Estimates from the National Health Interview Survey, United States, 1990.

Table 6.3

Workdays Lost Due to Acute Conditions (1988–1989)

	Number of work-loss days (millions)						Work-loss days per employed person					
	All ages 18 or more		Age 18 to 44		Age 45 or more		All ages 18 or more		Age 18 to 44		Age 45 or more	
Total	1988	1989	1988	1989	1988	1989	1988	1989	1988	1989	1988	1989
All acute conditions	358	395	271	298	87	96	3.1	3.4	3.3	3.6	2.5	2.7
Infectious/parasitic diseases	29	23	25	20	3	4	0.2	0.2	0.3	0.2	0.1	0.1
Respiratory conditions	127	148	94	111	32	37	1.1	1.2	1.1	1.3	0.1	1.1
Digestive system conditions	14	12	11	8	2	4	0.1	0.1	0.1	0.2	0.1	0.1
Injuries	109	124	81	99	27	26	0.1	1.1	0.1	0.2	0.1	0.7
Selected other acute conditions	—	63	—	49	—	14	—	0.5	—	0.6	—	0.4
All other acute conditions	21	23	11	12	9	11	0.2	0.2	0.1	0.2	0.2	0.3
Male												
All acute conditions	175	188	130	138	45	49	2.7	2.9	2.9	3.1	2.3	2.5
Infectious/parasitic diseases	13	10	11	10	1	1	0.2	0.2	0.2	0.2	0.1	0.1
Respiratory conditions	58	64	42	47	15	17	0.9	1.0	0.9	1.0	0.8	0.9
Digestive system conditions	7	6	6	3	1	3	0.1	0.9	0.1	0.1	0.1	0.1
Injuries	74	81	57	64	17	17	1.1	1.3	1.2	1.4	0.9	0.9
Selected other acute conditions	—	15	—	10	—	6	—	0.2	—	0.2	—	0.3
All other acute conditions	9	10	5	4	4	6	0.1	0.2	0.1	0.1	0.2	0.3
Female												
All acute conditions	183	207	141	160	42	46	3.5	3.9	3.8	4.3	2.8	3.0
Infectious/parasitic diseases	15	13	13	10	2	2	0.2	0.2	0.3	0.3	0.1	0.1
Respiratory conditions	69	84	52	64	17	20	1.3	1.6	1.4	1.7	1.1	1.3
Digestive system conditions	7	6	5	5	1	1	0.1	0.1	0.1	0.1	0.1	0.1
Injuries	35	44	24	34	10	9	0.6	0.8	0.6	0.9	0.7	0.6
Selected other acute conditions	—	47	—	39	—	8	—	3.9	—	1.0	—	0.5
All other acute conditions	11	13	6	8	4	5	0.2	0.2	0.1	0.2	0.3	0.3

— = No data are available.

NOTES: The data refer to the civilian noninstitutionalized population. An acute condition is one that lasted fewer than 3 months and that involved either medical attention or restricted activity. A "work-loss" day is a day on which a currently employed person, 18 years of age or more, did not work at least half of his or her normal workday because of a specific illness or injury. In some cases the sum of the items does not equal the total shown because of rounding.

SOURCE: U.S. Department of Health and Human Services, National Center for Health Statistics, Current Estimates from the National Health Interview Survey, United States, 1988 and 1989.

Table 6.4

Number of Occupational Injuries and Illnesses, and Lost Workdays in the Private Sector by Industry Division (1988– 1989) (Thousands)

Industry division	Total cases*		Lost workday cases		Lost workdays	
	1988	1989	1988	1989	1988	1989
Injuries and illnesses						
Private sector	6,440.4	6,576.3	2,977.8	3,073.9	56,996.1	60,123.7
Agriculture, forestry, and fishing**	101.9	102.3	52.7	53.3	952.1	946.4
Mining	64.4	60.6	37.7	34.5	1,113.2	976.4
Construction	655.2	646.5	307.2	304.8	6,381.4	6,464.2
Manufacturing	2,463.9	2,465.5	1,079.6	1,093.7	20,264.8	21,311,3
Durable goods	1,597.1	1,581.6	669.5	673.4	12,520.6	13,081.2
Nondurable goods	866.8	883.8	410.1	420.2	7,744.2	8,230.1
Transportation and public utilities	464.6	481.0	264.5	277.3	6,170.5	6,341.4
Wholesale and retail trade	1,533.4	1,603.3	683.4	719.2	11,914.2	12,767.4
Wholesale trade	434.2	455.8	217.6	233.3	3,941.5	4,232.8
Retail trade	1,009.1	1,147.4	465.7	485.9	7,972.7	8,531.6
Finance, insurance, and real estate	119.5	118.6	55.6	54.5	1,024.6	1,055.0
Services	1,037.6	1,098.5	497.1	536.6	9.175.2	10,261.6
Injuries						
Private sector	6,199.6	6,292.5	2,880.4	2,955.5	54,339.7	56,704.9
Agriculture, forestry, and fishing**	97.3	98.0	51.3	52.2	933.2	932.6
Mining	62.5	58.6	37.1	33.9	1,100.3	958.4
Construction	648.3	638.8	304.4	301.2	6,338.4	6,386.0
Manufacturing	2,287.2	2,261.0	1,007.6	1,007.4	18,194.5	18,627.5
Durable goods	1,479.5	1,453.5	625.0	623.7	11,203.5	11,509.6
Nondurable goods	807.8	807.5	382.3	383.7	6,991.0	7,117.9
Transportation and public utilities	455.6	472.6	261.3	273.9	6,103.2	6,266.6
Wholesale and retail trade	1,518.1	1,583.6	676.3	710.9	11,689.2	12,550.9
Wholesale trade	427.8	447.0	214.7	230.3	3,882.5	4,161.4
Retail trade	1,090.3	1,136.5	461.6	480.6	7,806.6	8,389.5
Finance, insurance, and real estate	116.3	115.0	54.0	52.6	970.4	988.3
Services	1,014.2	1,064.9	488.6	523.4	9,010.5	9,994.7
Illnesses						
Private sector	240.8	283.7	97.4	118.4	2,656.4	3,418.8
Agriculture, forestry, and fishing**	4.6	4.3	1.4	1.1	18.9	13.9
Mining	1.9	2.0	0.6	0.6	12.8	18.0
Construction	6.9	7.7	2.8	3.6	43.0	75.2
Manufacturing	176.6	204.5	72.2	86.3	2,070.2	2,683.7
Durable goods	117.7	128.1	44.4	49.8	1,317.1	1,571.6
Nondurable goods	59.0	76.3	27.8	36.5	753.1	1,112.2
Transportation and public utilities	9.0	8.4	3.2	3.4	67.4	74.8
Wholesale and retail trade	15.2	19.7	7.1	8.2	225.1	216.5
Wholesale trade	6.5	8.8	3.0	3.0	59.0	71.4
Retail trade	8.8	10.9	4.1	5.2	166.1	145.1
Finance, insurance, and real estate	3.1	3.7	1.6	2.0	54.2	66.7
Services	23.5	33.6	8.5	13.2	164.7	266.9

* Includes fatalities.
** Excludes farms with fewer than 11 employees.

NOTES: Because of rounding, components may not add to the totals. The difference between the number of total cases and the sum of the lost workday cases and nonfatal cases without lost workdays may not equal the fatalities.

SOURCE: U.S. Department of Labor, Bureau of Labor Statistics.

Table 6.5

Occupational Injury and Illness Incidence Rates Per 100 Full-Time Employees (1972–1989)

Year	Total cases	Cases with lost workdays	Nonfatal cases without lost workdays	Lost workdays
1972	10.9	3.3	7.6	47.9
1973	11.0	3.4	7.5	53.3
1974	10.4	3.4	6.9	54.6
1975	9.1	3.3	5.8	56.1
1976	9.2	3.5	5.7	60.5
1977	9.3	3.8	5.5	61.6
1978	9.4	4.1	5.3	63.5
1979	9.5	4.3	5.2	67.7
1980	8.7	4.0	4.7	65.2
1981	8.3	3.8	4.5	61.7
1982	7.7	3.5	4.2	58.7
1983	7.6	3.4	4.2	58.5
1984	7.0	3.7	4.3	63.4
1985	7.9	3.6	4.3	64.9
1986	7.9	3.6	4.3	65.8
1987	8.3	3.8	4.4	69.9
1988	8.6	4.0	4.6	76.1
1989	8.6	4.0	4.6	78.7

SOURCE: U.S. Department of Labor, Bureau of Labor Statistics.

Table 6.6

Growth in the Social Security Disability Program (1965–1989)

Year	Number of workers insured for disability (millions)	Number of workers receiving benefits (millions)	Number of beneficiaries per 100,000 insured workers	Total disability insurance beneficiaries (millions)	Total cash benefits paid for disability (billions)
1965	53.3	1.0	1,954	1.7	1.6
1966	55.0	1.1	1,995	1.9	1.8
1967	55.7	1.2	2,142	2.1	1.9
1968	56.9	1.3	2,276	2.3	2.3
1969	70.1	1.4	1,989	2.5	2.5
1970	72.4	1.5	2,062	2.7	3.1
1971	74.5	1.6	2,212	2.9	3.8
1972	76.1	1.8	2,409	3.3	4.5
1973	77.8	2.0	2,592	3.6	5.7
1974	80.4	2.2	2,782	3.9	6.9
1975	83.3	2.5	2,988	4.4	8.4
1976	85.3	2.7	3,130	4.6	10.0
1977	87.0	2.8	3,261	4.9	11.5
1978	89.3	2.9	3,225	4.9	12.5
1979	93.7	2.9	3,064	4.8	13.7
1980	98.0	2.9	2,917	4.7	15.4
1981	100.5	2.8	2,763	4.5	17.2
1982	102.4	2.6	2,543	4.0	17.3
1983	104.0	2.6	2,470	3.8	17.5
1984	105.0	2.6	2,472	3.8	17.9
1985	106.7	2.7	2,490	3.9	18.8
1986	109.3	2.7	2,495	3.9	19.8
1987	111.5	2.8	2,499	4.0	20.5
1988	113.9	2.8	2,485	4.1	21.7
1989	115.9	2.9	2,499	4.1	22.9

NOTES: Number of disabled workers in current status as of December 31 of the year indicated. Insured workers as of January 1 of the year indicated.
SOURCE: U.S. Department of Health and Human Services. Social Security Administration.

Table 6.7

Life Expectancy at Birth (1980 – 1988)

Year of birth	All races		White		Black	
	Male	Female	Male	Female	Male	Female
1980	70.0	77.4	70.7	78.1	63.8	72.5
1981	70.4	77.8	71.1	78.4	64.5	73.2
1982	70.9	78.1	71.5	78.7	65.1	73.7
1983	71.0	78.1	71.7	78.7	65.4	73.6
1984	71.2	78.2	71.8	78.7	65.6	73.7
1985	71.2	78.2	71.9	78.7	65.3	73.5
1986	71.3	78.3	72.0	78.8	65.2	73.5
1987	71.5	78.3	72.2	78.9	65.2	73.6
1988	71.5	78.3	72.3	78.9	64.9	73.4

SOURCE: U.S. Department of Health and Human Services, National Center for Health Statistics, Monthly Vital Statistics Report, November 28, 1990.

Table 6.8

AIDS Cases Diagnosed and Deaths Occurring Before 1981 Through 1990

Year of diagnosis	Adults and adolescents		Children under 13 years	
	Cases	Deaths	Cases	Deaths
Total	168,590	106,749	2,984	1,562
Before 1981	79	30	6	1
1981	295	104	14	8
1982	1,078	435	29	14
1983	2,912	1,440	76	29
1984	5,903	3,310	110	49
1985	11,057	6,545	221	112
1986	18,036	11,264	318	150
1987	26,849	15,076	467	271
1988	32,421	19,214	560	288
1989	36,255	24,991	624	330
1990	33,705	24,134	559	305

NOTE: Death totals include 186 adults/adolescents and 5 children known to have died, but whose dates of death are unknown.
SOURCE: U.S. Department of Health and Human Services, Centers for Disease Control, HIV/AIDS Surveillance Report.

Table 6.9

Causes of Death (1988)

Cause of death	Deaths per 100,000 population	Percent of total deaths
Diseases of the heart	311.3	35.3
Malignant neoplasms	197.3	22.4
Cerebrovascular diseases	61.2	6.9
Accidents and adverse effects	39.5	4.5
Chronic obstructive pulmonary disease and allied conditions	33.7	3.8
Pneumonia and influenza	31.6	3.6
Diabetes mellitus	16.4	1.9
Suicide	12.4	1.4
Chronic liver disease and cirrhosis	10.7	1.2
Nephritis, nephrotic syndrome	9.1	1.0
Atherosclerosis	9.0	1.0
Homicide and legal intervention	9.0	1.0
Septicemia	8.5	1.0
Conditions originating in perinatal period	7.4	0.8
AIDS	6.8	0.8
All other causes	118.1	13.4

SOURCE: National Center for Health Statistics, Monthly Vital Statistics Report, November 28, 1990.

Table 6.10

Deaths from the Four Leading Causes by State (1988)

States	Heart	Cancer	Stroke	All accidents including suicide
Total United States	765,156	485,048	150,517	176,585
Alabama	13,272	8,459	2,922	3,882
Alaska	465	449	86	551
Arizona	8,776	6,280	1,532	3,299
Arkansas	8,607	5,409	2,128	2,194
California	70,636	47,714	15,993	20,093
Colorado	6,477	4,452	1,324	2,298
Connecticut	10,308	6,851	1,742	1,834
Delaware	2,045	1,437	295	532
District of Columbia	2,196	1,628	398	369
Florida	46,922	31,205	8,823	10,559
Georgia	16,911	10,859	4,038	5,744
Hawaii	1,837	1,529	430	548
Idaho	2,378	1,593	603	970
Illinois	39,581	23,494	6,953	7,700
Indiana	17,670	11,353	3,891	3,922
Iowa	10,181	6,190	2,214	2,067
Kansas	8,055	4,979	1,779	1,820
Kentucky	12,596	8,026	2,569	3,068
Louisiana	13,357	8,410	2,574	3,507
Maine	3,981	2,731	777	884
Maryland	12,765	9,290	2,371	2,862
Massachusetts	20,251	13,156	3,742	3,041
Michigan	30,230	17,909	5,251	6,149
Minnesota	11,907	8,107	3,010	2,660
Mississippi	9,240	5,277	1,994	2,516
Missouri	18,472	10,933	3,653	4,006
Montana	2,071	1,543	459	717
Nebraska	5,149	3,165	1,158	1,080
Nevada	2,722	2,067	416	987
New Hampshire	3,020	2,118	610	606
New Jersey	27,491	17,253	4,241	4,103
New Mexico	2,860	2,180	633	1,683
New York	67,365	38,675	9,665	9,389
North Carolina	19,428	12,705	4,777	5,606
North Dakota	2,058	1,285	431	431
Ohio	37,402	23,020	6,739	6,766
Oklahoma	11,009	6,398	2,305	2,543
Oregon	7,778	5,827	2,005	2,412
Pennsylvania	48,081	28,453	8,076	7,997
Rhode Island	3,511	2,403	636	540
South Carolina	10,197	6,144	2,593	3,327
South Dakota	2,595	1,354	522	518
Tennessee	16,043	9,846	3,730	4,365
Texas	40,847	25,906	8,174	12,275
Utah	2,963	1,780	690	1,127
Vermont	1,612	1,021	317	438
Virginia	16,156	11,009	3,519	4,010
Washington	11,744	83,336	2,797	3,341
West Virginia	7,450	4,347	1,310	1,605
Wisconsin	15,569	9,810	3,388	3,185
Wyoming	919	698	234	459

SOURCE: National Center for Health Statistics. Monthly Vital Statistics Report, November 28, 1990.

Table 6.11

Trends in Death Rates (1920–1989)

Death rates and causes	1920	1940	1960	1980	1987	1988	1989
Death rates (per 100,000 population)	**1,298.9**	**1,076.4**	**954.7**	**874.1**	**872.4**	**883**	**868.1**
Major causes of death							
Pneumonia and influenza	207.3	70.3	37.3	23.2	28.4	31.5	30.3
Diseases of the heart	159.6	292.5	369.0	335.9	312.4	312.2	296.3
Tuberculosis	113.1	45.9	6.1	*	*	0.8	0.7
Cerebrovascular diseases	93.0	90.9	108.0	75.0	61.6	61.1	59.4
Malignant neoplasms	83.4	120.3	149.2	182.4	195.9	198.6	200.3
Accidents	71.0	73.6	52.3	46.9	39.0	39.7	38.2
Infant mortality							
(per 1,000 live births)	NA	47.0	26.0	12.5	10.1	9.9	9.7
Maternal mortality							
(per 100,000 live births)	NA	376.0	37.1	6.9	6.6	0.1	0.1

*Not listed as a major cause of death.

SOURCE: National Center for Health Statistics, Monthly Vital Statistics Report, August 30, 1990.

HEALTH AND HEALTH CARE ACRONYMS

ACLI	American Council of Life Insurance
ADA	American Dental Association
AD&D	Accidental Death & Dismemberment Policy
AHA	American Hospital Association
AHCPR	Agency for Health Care Policy and Research
AIDS	Acquired Immune Deficiency Syndrome
AMA	American Medical Association
ANA	American Nurses Association
APA	American Pharmaceutical Association
ASO	Administrative Services Only
BCBS	Blue Cross-Blue Shield
BLS	Bureau of Labor Statistics
CDC	Centers for Disease Control
CHAMPUS	Civilian Health and Medical Program of the Uniformed Services
COB	Coordination of Benefits
COBRA	Consolidated Omnibus Budget Reconciliation Act
CON	Certificate of Need
CPI	Consumer Price Index
CPR	Cardiopulmonary Resuscitation
CPT	Current Procedural Terminology
DOL	Department of Labor
DRG	Diagnosis-Related Group
EBRI	Employee Benefit Research Institute
EOB	Explanation of Benefits
EPO	Exclusive Provider Organization
ERISA	Employee Retirement Income Security Act
FEHBP	Federal Employees Health Benefits Program
FFS	Fee for Service
GAO	General Accounting Office
GDP	Gross Domestic Product
GHAA	Group Health Association of America
GNP	Gross National Product
HCFA	Health Care Financing Administration

HCPCS	HCFA Common Procedural Coding System
HHS	Health and Human Services
HIAA	Health Insurance Association of America
HIV	Human Immunosuppressant Virus
HMO	Health Maintenance Organization
ICD	International Classification of Diseases
IPA	Independent Practice Association
LHD	Local Health Departments
LOS	Length of Stay
LTC	Long-Term Care
LTD	Long-Term Disability
MMPS	Medical Mortality Prediction System
MPP	Minimum Premium Plan
NAHDO	National Association of Health Data Organizations
NAIC	National Association of Insurance Commissioners
NCHS	National Center for Health Statistics
NCHSR	National Center for Health Services Research
NHC	National Health Council
NIH	National Institutes of Health
NIMH	National Institute of Mental Health
OBRA	Omnibus Budget Reconciliation Act
OECD	Organization for Economic Cooperation and Development
POS	Point of Service
PPO	Preferred Provider Organization
PPRC	Physician Payment Review Commission
PPS	Prospective Payment System
ProPAC	Prospective Payment Review Assessment Commission
RBRVS	Resource Based Relative Value System
SHA	State Health Agency
SNF	Skilled Nursing Facility
SSA	Social Security Administration
STD	Sexually Transmitted Disease
STD	Short-Term Disability
TEFRA	Tax Equity and Fiscal Responsibility Act
TPA	Third-Party Administrator
TPP	Third-Party Payer
UCR	Usual, Customary, and Reasonable
UR	Utilization Review
WHO	World Health Organization

HISTORICAL INSURANCE FACTS

1798 U.S. Marine Hospital Service established by U.S. Congress. Compulsory deductions for hospital service were made from seamen's wages.

1847 The first insurer to issue sickness insurance was organized: The Massachusetts Health Insurance Company of Boston.

1849 New York State passed the first general insurance law.

1850s The first insurance supervisory boards were created in New Hampshire, Massachusetts, Rhode Island and Vermont.

1850 Individual accident insurance became available in the United States with the chartering of the Franklin Health Assurance Company in Massachusetts.

1851 One of the earliest voluntary mutual protection associations, *La Société Française de Bienfaisance Mutuelle*, was organized in San Francisco. It is noteworthy for having established a hospital in 1852 to provide for its members.

1855 The first separate insurance department, independent of any established agency, was created in Massachusetts.

1859 The first full-time insurance commissioner was appointed in New York.

1863 The Travelers Insurance Company of Hartford, Connecticut, offered accident insurance for railway mishaps; then, all forms of accident protection. It was the first company to issue insurance on a basis resembling its present form.

1875 A number of mutual benefit associations, called "establishment funds," were formed for employees of a single employer. The benefits provided usually included small payments for death and disability.

1890s This period brought the promotion of many fraternal associations, assessment mutuals and industrial insurers. Because many of these companies and associations were inadequately financed and poorly managed, many states passed legislation against them.

1890 Policies providing benefits for disability from specified diseases were first offered.

1900 Shortly after the turn of the century, disability benefits became available for substantially all diseases.

1910 Montgomery Ward & Co., Inc., replaced its "employee establishment fund" with an insured contract. This plan is generally regarded as the first group health insurance policy.

1912 The Standard Provisions Law drafted by the National Convention of Insurance Commissioners (now the NAIC) was enacted by most states. This model law sought to provide uniformity and fairness in the "operating conditions" of the health insurance contract.

1916 First noncancelable disability income contract was offered.

1917 Group accidental death and dismemberment insurance was first written.

1920s Early in this decade individual hospitals began offering hospital expense benefits on an individual prepaid basis.

1920s First partial disability benefits for sickness and accident became available.

1929 The first health maintenance organization, the Ross-Loos Clinic, was established in Los Angeles, California.

1929 A group of school teachers arranged for Baylor Hospital in Dallas, Texas, to provide room and board and specified ancillary services at a predetermined monthly cost. This plan is considered the forerunner of what later became known as the Blue Cross plans.

1929 With the Depression, many companies entered a period of retrenchment in their disability income product line, particularly in the area of maintaining reasonable indemnity limits in order to avoid overinsurance.

1930s The Depression stimulated the expansion of insurance coverages through both public demand and hospitals' encouragement.

1932 First citywide Blue Cross plan was tried out with a group of hospitals in Sacramento, California.

1935 The Social Security Act (P.L. 74-241) provided for the first time grant-in-aid to states for such public health activities as maternal and child care, aid to crippled children, blind persons, the aged and other health-impaired persons.

1937 Health Service Plan Commission (Blue Cross Commission) was organized.

1938 Hospital insurance for dependents of covered persons was developed.

1938 Private insurers introduced group surgical expense benefit plans.

1939 The first Blue Shield plan (surgical-medical), called the California Physicians' Service, was developed.

1940s During World War II, as a result of the freezing of wages, group health insurance became an important component of collective bargaining for employee benefits.

1942 Compulsory cash sickness benefits were begun by four states (Rhode Island, 1942; California, 1946; New Jersey, 1948; New York, 1949).

1943 Private insurers introduced group medical expense benefits (physicians' visits expense benefits).

1946 The Health Insurance Council, a federation of eight insurance associations organized to give technical and practical assistance on health insurance to the providers of medical care, was formed.

1946 Blue Shield Medical Care Plans, Inc. (Blue Shield Commission) was organized.

1948 The National Labor Relations Board ruled, in a dispute between the United Steelworkers' Union and the Inland Steel Company, that the term "wages" be construed to include pension and insurance benefits. The U.S. Supreme Court upheld this ruling in a 1949 decision.

1949 Major medical expense benefits were introduced by Liberty Mutual Insurance Company to supplement basic medical care expenses.

1954 Congress introduced the disability "freeze" that stated that the quarters during which a worker is disabled are not counted in determining the number of quarters needed to be fully or currently insured under Old Age and Survivors Insurance (OASI).

1956 Disability insurance was added to the Social Security System, providing monthly cash benefits for insured persons who are totally disabled.

1957 Vision care expense benefits were introduced by private insurers, followed in 1959 by extended care facility expense benefits.

1959 Continental Casualty Company issued the first comprehensive group dental insurance plan written by an insurance company.

1960s First disability contracts for business use appeared (overhead expense, key man).

1960s Eligibility for disability benefits under Social Security was expanded.

1961 First state enrollment plan was made available by Connecticut to persons aged 65 and more on a state basis and under special enabling legislation allowing the pooling of risks by a group of insurance companies (Associated Connecticut Health Insurance Companies).

1963 The Health Profession Educational Assistance Act (P.L. 88-129) aided training of physicians, dentists and other public health personnel.

1964 Prescription drug expense benefits were introduced.

1964 The Nurse Training Act (P.L. 88-581) provided special federal effort for training professional nursing personnel.

1965 Social Security Amendments of 1965 (P.L. 89-97) established a Social Security hospital insurance program for the aged and a voluntary supplementary medical insurance program (Medicare) and grants to states for medical assistance programs (Medicaid).

1966 Program of governmental health insurance, Medicare, for people aged 65 and more, became effective July 1.

1967　The Age Discrimination in Employment Act (ADEA) became effective.

● The act applied only to employees between the ages of 40 and 65, and the vast majority of employee benefit plans provided them with the same benefits as younger employees.

● The act contained a specific provision (Section 4(f)(2)) which stated that it was permissible for an employer to observe the terms of any bona fide employee benefit plan such as a retirement, pension or insurance plan which was not a subterfuge to evade the purposes of the act.

1971　The Insurance Medical Scientist Scholarship Fund was formed by several insurance companies, providing full scholarships for students planning careers in medical research and teaching.

1972　Social Security Amendments of 1972 (P.L. 92-603) extended health insurance benefits (Medicare) to the disabled and to end-stage renal disease patients, established Professional Standards Review Organization (PSRO) programs, expanded research and demonstrations of financing mechanisms and introduced automatic cost-of-living adjustments to disability benefits.

1972　Legislation created the Supplemental Security Income program, which federalized categorical public assistance for the aged, blind and permanently and totally disabled.

1973　The Health Maintenance Organization Act (P.L. 93-222) assisted in the establishment and expansion of HMOs.

1974　Employee Retirement Income Security Act (ERISA) of 1974 was signed into law. While generally thought of as a law that regulates private pension plans, the act also contains provisions relating to other employee benefit plans that have encouraged the growth of self-insurance.

1975　The National Health Planning and Resources Development Act of 1974 (P.L. 93-641) authorized major federal reorganization of health planning programs and set up the national designation of local Health Systems Areas and governing agencies.

1976　The Health Professions Educational Assistance Act of 1976 (P.L. 94-484) contained provisions requiring medical school students who receive federal scholarship aid to serve a specified period in rural and inner city areas, and required that medical schools with teaching hospitals provide for a greater proportion of medical residencies in primary medicine.

1976　The Health Maintenance Organization Amendments of 1976 (P.L. 94-460) relaxed requirements for HMOs to qualify for federal support.

1976 The National Consumer Health Information and Health Promotion Act of 1976 (P.L. 94-317) set forth national goals for health information and promotion and a systematic strategy for their achievement, stressing health education.

1977 The Medicare-Medicaid Anti-Fraud and Abuse Amendments (P.L. 95-142) amended the Social Security Act to require uniform reporting of financial data by providers, upgraded criminal penalties for fraud under Medicare-Medicaid programs and amended certain Professional Standards Review Organization (PSRO) provisions.

1978 The Health Maintenance Organization Amendments of 1978 (P.L. 95-559) set forth a three-year extension of the HMO assistance program.

1978 Title VII of the Civil Rights Act of 1964 was amended to prohibit sex discrimination on the basis of pregnancy for all employment-related purposes.

1978 ADEA of 1967 was amended to raise the mandatory retirement age from 65 to 70. The act prohibits discrimination concerning benefits to older workers. An employer may coordinate benefits with other programs—e.g., Medicare for employees over age 65—provided that total benefits are equivalent to those offered younger workers.

1981 The Omnibus Budget Reconciliation Act mandated significant cuts in federal expenditures for health programs, increased Medicare deductibles, removed the limit on the number of states that can apply for Medicare and Medicaid cost reimbursement waivers and directed the Secretary of HHS to develop a model prospective reimbursement methodology for inpatient services under Medicare and Medicaid.

1982 Tax Equity and Fiscal Responsibility Act (TEFRA) of 1982 provided Medicare recognition for any state hospital cost-control system that meets certain federal standards (including equitable treatment of all payers) and for employees aged 65–69 with employer-sponsored health insurance. It made Medicare the secondary payer, brought federal employees under Medicare and made certain changes in the methods of hospital reimbursements under Medicare.

1983 In response to the requirement of the Tax Equity and Fiscal Responsibility Act (TEFRA) of 1982, a prospective payment system for hospital care of Medicare enrollees was enacted as a component of the Social Security Amendments of 1983.

1984 Omnibus Deficit Reduction Act of 1984 (P.L. 98-369) extended Medicare as secondary payer of aged spouses of workers under age 65, froze Medicare reimbursement for physician fees and reduced increases in hospital costs.

1984 National Organ Transplant Act of 1984 (P.L. 98-507) established a task force on organ transplantation, authorized grants for organ procurement organizations and established bone marrow registry demonstration and study.

1985 Consolidated Omnibus Budget Reconciliation Act of 1985 (P.L. 99-272) required that employer group health plans offer continued coverage to workers and their dependents upon termination of employment, and to workers' spouses and dependents who would lose such coverage due to death of the worker, divorce and Medicare eligibility; made private employer health plans primary to Medicare for active workers and their spouses who also have Medicare coverage; required that third-party payers reimburse for certain care rendered in government-run veterans and military hospitals; and established a task force to study long-term care insurance policies.

1986 Tax Reform Act of 1986 (P.L. 99-514) removed the federal tax exemption for Blue Cross-Blue Shield organizations engaged in providing commercial-type insurance, established uniform nondiscrimination rules for group health insur-

ance plans and restored a partial, 25 percent tax deduction for health insurance premiums for self-employed individuals and their employees.

1986 Omnibus Budget Reconciliation Act of 1986 (P.L. 99-509) made private employer health plans primary to Medicare for beneficiaries eligible by reason of permanent disability in cases where the disabled person is a covered dependent under a working spouse's health plan or if the disabled person returns to active employment and revised the formula for determining Medicare's Part A deductible.

1986 ADEA for 1967 was further amended to prohibit mandating retirement at any age; employer-provided benefits for older workers must be equal to those for younger workers.

1988 The Health Maintenance Organization Amendments of 1988 (P.L. 100-51) provided greatly enhanced flexibility to federally qualified HMOs for structuring their organizations and for calculating premiums. Employers were also permitted to base their contributions to federally qualified HMOs on the projected claims experience of employees joining the HMO.

1988 The Medicare Catastrophic Coverage Act of 1988 (P.L. 100-360) represented the largest expansion in the Medicare program since its inception in 1965. Benefit changes included the elimination of all cost sharing for inpatient hospital care after the hospital deductible, a cap on out-of-pocket expenses for physicians' services of $1,370 and minor changes in skilled nursing, home health and respite care benefits. A phased-in outpatient drug benefit will be added to Medicare in 1991. Employers offering retiree health benefits to Medicare beneficiaries must rebate in cash or new benefits the actuarial value of the new catastrophic benefits for one year.

1988 Congress passed AIDS-related legislation containing funds for research, education, HIV testing and home health demonstration projects.

1989 The Omnibus Budget Reconciliation Act of 1989, Title VI of H.R. 3299, contained a provision requiring states to extend Medicaid coverage to all pregnant women and children up to age 6 with family incomes up to 133 percent of federal poverty level ($13,380 for a family of three) by April 1, 1990. The act (P.L. 101-239) also included a three-part plan to reform the physician payment system under Medicare.

1989 The Medicare Catastrophic Coverage Act of 1988 (P.L. 100-360) was repealed.

GLOSSARY

Accident. An event or occurrence which is unforeseen and unintended.

Accidental Bodily Injury. Injury to the body as the result of an accident.

Accumulation Period. A specified period of time, such as 90 days, during which the insured person must incur eligible medical expenses at least equal to the deductible amount in order to establish a benefit period under a major medical expense or comprehensive medical expense policy.

Actuary. A person professionally trained to apply probability and statistics to the practical problems of insurance and related fields. He/she may specialize in life insurance, health insurance (long-term disability and medical), property and casualty insurance, pension work, government programs, or a combination of these. His/her responsibilities include calculation of premiums, policy values, reserves and dividends, preparation of statistical studies, and forecasting of financial results. Because of his/her broad training, an actuary often has administrative and executive responsibilities.

Administrative Services Only (ASO) Plan. An arrangement under which an insurance carrier or an independent organization will, for a fee, handle the administration of claims, benefits and other administrative functions for a self-insured group.

Adverse Selection. The tendency of persons with poorer than average health expectations to apply for, or continue, insurance to a greater extent than do persons with average or better health expectations.

Age Limits. Stipulated minimum and maximum ages below and above which the company will not accept applications or may not renew policies.

Agent. An insurance company representative licensed by the state who solicits, negotiates or effects contracts of insurance, and provides service to the policyholder for the insurer.

Aggregate Indemnity. The maximum dollar amount that may be collected for any disability or period of disability under the policy.

AIDS. Acquired immune deficiency syndrome. A fatal, incurable disease caused by a virus that can damage the brain and destroy the body's ability to fight off illness. AIDS poses major problems for insurers, policyholders, and the whole of society.

Allocated Benefits. Benefits for which the maximum amount payable for specific services is itemized in the contract.

Alternate Delivery Systems. Health services provided in other than an inpatient, acute-care hospital. Examples include skilled and intermediary nursing facilities, hospice programs, and home health care. Alternate delivery systems are designed to provide needed services in a more cost-effective manner.

Ambulatory Care. Medical services that are provided on an outpatient (nonhospitalized) basis. Services may include diagnosis, treatment, and rehabilitation.

Amendment. A formal document changing the provisions of an insurance policy signed jointly by the insurance company officer and the policy holder or his authorized representative.

Application. A signed statement of facts requested by the company on the basis of which the company decides whether or not to issue a policy. This then becomes part of the health insurance contract when the policy is issued.

Approval. (1) Word used in connection with the filing of policy and certificate forms and rates with the state insurance department. (2) A word used in connection with the underwriting process of an insurance company, consisting of the acceptance of the risk as set forth in the application as made or modified by the insurer. (3) Acceptance of an offer from an applicant or policyholder in the form of a contract for new insurance, reinstatement of a terminated policy, request for a policy loan, etc., by an officer of the company.

Assignment. The signed transfer of benefits of a policy by the owner of the policy to a third party.

Association Group. A group formed from members of a trade or a professional association for group insurance under one master health insurance contract.

Beneficiary. The person designated or provided for by the policy terms to receive the proceeds upon the death of the insured.

Benefits. The amount payable by the insurance company to a claimant, assignee or beneficiary under each coverage.

Binding Receipt. A receipt given for a premium payment accompanying the application for insurance. If the policy is approved, this binds the company to make the policy effective from the date of the receipt.

Blanket Contract. A contract of health insurance affording benefits, such as accidental death and dismemberment, for all of a class of persons not individually identified. It is used for such groups as athletic teams, campers, travel policy for employees, etc.

Blanket Medical Expense. A provision which entitles the insured person to collect up to a maximum established in the policy for all hospital and medical expenses incurred, without any limitations on individual types of medical expenses.

Blue Cross. An independent, nonprofit membership corporation providing protection on a service basis against the cost of hospital care in a limited geographical area.

Blue Shield. An independent, nonprofit membership corporation providing protection on a service basis against the cost of surgical and medical care in a limited geographical area.

Broker. A sales and service representative who handles insurance for clients, generally selling insurance of various kinds and for several companies.

Business Insurance. A policy which primarily provides coverage of benefits to a business as contrasted to an individual. It is issued to indemnify a business for the loss of services of a key employee or a partner who becomes disabled.

Capitation. A method of payment for health services in which a physician or hospital is paid a fixed, per capita amount for each person served regardless of the actual number of services provided to each person.

Certificate of Insurance. A statement of coverage issued to an individual insured under a group insurance contract, outlining the insurance benefits and principal provisions applicable to the member.

Claim. A demand to the insurer for the payment of benefits under the insurance contract.

Coinsurance. A policy provision frequently found in major medical insurance, by which both the insured person and the insurer share the covered losses under a policy in a specified ratio, i.e., 80 percent by the insurer and 20 percent by the insured.

Comprehensive Major Medical Insurance. A policy designed to give

the protection offered by both a basic and a major medical health insurance policy. It is characterized by a low deductible amount, a coinsurance feature, and high maximum benefits.

Consideration. One of the elements for a binding contract. Consideration is acceptance by the insurance company of the payment of the premium and the statement made by the prospective policyholder in the application.

Contributory. A group insurance plan issued to an employer under which both the employer and employee contribute to the cost of the plan. Seventy-five percent of the eligible employees must be insured. (See Noncontributory.)

Conversion Privilege. A privilege granted in an insurance policy to convert to a different plan of insurance without providing evidence of insurability. The privilege granted by a group policy is to convert to an individual policy upon termination of group coverage.

Coordination of Benefits (COB). The specific term used to designate the antiduplication provision designed by the group health insurance industry through the Health Insurance Association of America (HIAA) to limit benefits for multiple group health insurance in a particular case to 100 percent of the expenses covered and to designate the order in which the multiple carriers are to pay benefits.

Cost Containment. The control or reduction of inefficiencies in the consumption, allocation, or production of health care services that contribute to higher than necessary costs.

Covered Expenses. Hospital, medical, and miscellaneous health care expenses incurred by the insured that entitle him/her to a payment of benefits under a health insurance policy. Found most often in connection with major medical plans, the term defines, by either description, reasonableness, or necessity to specify the type and amount of expense which will be considered in the calculation of benefits.

Deductible. The amount of covered charges incurred by the protected person which must be assumed or paid by the insured before benefits by the insurance company become payable. A deductible is most commonly used in major medical policies; however, it may also be incorporated in base plan policies.

Diagnosis-Related Groups (DRGs). System that reimburses health care providers fixed amounts for all care given in connection with standard diagnostic categories.

Disability. Physical or mental handicap resulting from sickness or injury. It may be partial or total. (See Partial Disability; Total Disability.)

Disability Income Insurance. A form of health insurance that provides periodic payments to replace income when an insured person is unable to work as a result of illness, injury, or disease.

Dismemberment. Loss of body members (limbs), or use thereof, or loss of sight due to injury.

Disposable Personal Income. The personal income less personal tax and nontax payments. It is the income available to people for spending and saving.

Double Indemnity. A policy provision usually associated with death, which doubles payment of a designated benefit when certain kinds of accidents occur.

Dread Disease Insurance. Insurance providing an unallocated benefit, subject to a maximum amount, for expenses incurred in connection with the treatment of specified diseases, such as cancer, poliomyelitis, encephalitis and spinal meningitis.

Duplication of Benefits. Overlapping or identical coverage of the same, insured under two or more health plans, usually the result of contracts of different insurance companies, service organizations, or prepayment plans; also known as multiple coverage.

Earned Premium. That portion of a policy's premium payment for which the protection of the policy has already been given. For example, an insurance company is considered to have earned 75 percent of an annual premium after a period of nine months of an annual term has elapsed.

Effective Date. The date on which the insurance under a policy begins.

Eligibility Date. The date on which an individual member of a specified group becomes eligible to apply for insurance under the (group life or health) insurance plan.

Eligible Employees. Those members of a group who have met the eligibility requirements under a group life or health insurance plan.

Eligibility Period. A specified length of time, frequently 31 days, following the eligibility date during which an individual member of a particular group will remain eligible to apply for insurance under a group life or health insurance policy without evidence of insurability.

Elimination Period. A period of time between the period of disability and the start of disability income insurance benefits, during which no benefits are payable. (See Waiting Period.)

Enrollment Card. A document signed by an employee as notice of his/her desire to participate in the benefits of a group insurance plan.

Evidence of Insurability. Any statement of proof of a person's physical condition and/or other factual information affecting his/her acceptance for insurance.

Exclusions. Specific conditions or circumstances listed in the policy for which the policy will not provide benefit payments.

Exclusive Provider Organization (EPO). People who belong to an EPO must receive their care from affiliated providers; services rendered by unaffiliated providers are not reimbursed.

Experience. A term used to describe the relationship, usually expressed as a percent or ratio, of premium to claims for a plan, coverage, or benefits for a stated time period.

Experience Rating. The process of determining the premium rate for a group risk, wholly or partially on the basis of that group's experience.

Experience Refund. A provision in most group policies for the return of premium to the policyholder because of lower than anticipated claims.

Family Expense Policy. A policy which insures both the policyholder and his/her immediate dependents (usually spouse and children).

Flat Schedule. A type of schedule in group insurance under which everyone is insured for the same benefits regardless of salary, position, or other circumstances.

Franchise Insurance. A form of insurance in which individual policies are issued to the employees of a common employer or the members of an association under an arrangement by which the employer or association agrees to collect the premiums and remit them to the insurer.

Fraternal Insurance. A cooperative type of insurance provided by social organizations for their members.

Geographic Divisions (in the United States)

NORTHEAST
New England: Connecticut, Maine, Massachusetts, New Hampshire, Rhode Island, Vermont

Middle Atlantic: New Jersey, New York, Pennsylvania
MIDWEST
East North Central: Illinois, Indiana, Michigan, Ohio, Wisconsin
West North Central: Iowa, Kansas, Minnesota, Missouri, Nebraska, North Dakota, South Dakota
SOUTH
South Atlantic: Delaware, District of Columbia, Florida, Georgia, Maryland, North Carolina, South Carolina, Virginia, West Virginia
East South Central: Alabama, Kentucky, Mississippi, Tennessee
West South Central: Arkansas, Louisiana, Oklahoma, Texas
WEST
Mountain: Arizona, Colorado, Idaho, Montana, Nevada, New Mexico, Utah, Wyoming
Pacific: Alaska, California, Hawaii, Oregon, Washington.

Grace Period. A specified period after a premium payment is due, in which the policyholder may make such payment, and during which the protection of the policy continues.

Group Contract. A contract of insurance made with an employer or other entity that covers a group of persons identified as individuals by reference to their relationship to the entity.

Guaranteed Renewable Contract. A contract that the insured person or entity has the right to continue in force by the timely payment of premiums for a substantial period of time, during which period the insurer has no right to make unilaterally any change in any provision of the contract, while the contract is in force,

other than a change in the premium rate for classes of policyholders.

Health Insurance. Protection which provides payment of benefits for covered sickness or injury. Included under this heading are various types of insurance such as accident insurance, disability income insurance, medical expense insurance, and accidental death and dismemberment insurance.

Health Maintenance Organization (HMO). An organization that provides a wide range of comprehensive health care services for a specified group at a fixed periodic payment. The HMO can be sponsored by the government, medical schools, hospitals, employers, labor unions, consumer groups, insurance companies, and hospital-medical plans.

Hospice. Health care facility providing medical care and support services such as counseling to terminally ill persons.

Hospital Expense Insurance. Health insurance protection against the cost of hospital care resulting from the illness or injury of the insured person.

Hospital Indemnity. A form of health insurance which provides a stipulated daily, weekly, or monthly indemnity during hospital confinement. The indemnity is payable on an unallocated basis without regard to the actual expense of hospital confinement.

Hospital Medical Insurance. A term used to indicate protection which provides benefits for the cost of any or all of the numerous health care services normally covered under various health care plans.

Incontestable Clause. An optional clause which may be used in noncancelable or guaranteed renewable health insurance contracts providing that the insurer may not contest the validity of the contract after it has been in force for two (sometimes three) years.

Incurred Claims. Incurred claims equal the claims paid during the policy year plus the claim reserves as of the end of the policy year, minus the corresponding reserves as of the beginning of the policy year. The difference between the year end and beginning of the year claim reserves is called the increase in reserves and may be added directly to the paid claims to produce the incurred claims.

Indemnity. Benefits paid in a predetermined amount in the event of a covered loss.

Individual Insurance. Policies which provide protection to the policyholder and/or his/her family. Sometimes called Personal Insurance as distinct from group and blanket insurance.

Injury Independent of All Other Means. An injury resulting from an accident, provided that the accident was not caused by an illness.

Insurable Risk. The conditions that make a risk insurable are (a) the peril insured against must produce a definite loss not under the control of the insured, (b) there must be a large number of homogeneous exposures subject to the same perils, (c) the loss must be calculable and the cost of insuring it must be economically feasible, (d) the peril must be unlikely to affect all insureds simultaneously, and (e) the loss produced by a risk must be definite and have a potential to be financially serious.

Insurance. Protection by written contract against the financial hazards (in whole or in part) of the happenings of specified fortuitous events.

Insurance Company. Any corporation primarily engaged in the business of furnishing insurance protection to the public.

Insuring Clause. The clause which sets forth the type of loss being covered by the policy and the parties to the insurance contract.

Integration. A coordination of the disability income insurance benefit with other disability income benefits, such as Social Security, through a specific formula to insure reasonable income replacement.

Key-Man or Key-Person Health Insurance. An individual or group insurance policy designed to protect a firm against the loss of income resulting from disability of a key employee.

Lapse. Termination of a policy upon the policyholder's failure to pay the premium within the time required.

Legal Reserve. The minimum reserve which a company must keep to meet future claims and obligations as they are calculated under the state insurance code.

Level Premium. A premium which remains unchanged throughout the life of a policy.

Lifetime Disability Benefit. A benefit to help replace income lost by an insured person as long as he/she is totally disabled, even for a lifetime.

Limited Policy. A contract which covers only certain specified diseases or accidents.

Long-Term Care. The continuum of broad-ranged maintenance and health services to the chronically ill, disabled, or retarded. Services may be provided on an inpatient (rehabilitation facility, nursing home, mental hospital), outpatient, or at-home basis.

Long-Term Disability Income Insurance. Insurance issued to an employer (group) or individual to provide a reasonable replacement of a portion of an employee's earned income lost through serious and prolonged illness or injury during the normal work career. (See also Integration.)

Major Medical Insurance. Health insurance to finance the expense of major illness and injury. Characterized by large benefit maximums ranging up to $250,000 or no limit, the insurance, above an initial deductible, reimburses the major part of all charges for hospital, doctor, private nurses, medical appliances, prescribed out-of-hospital treatment, drugs, and medicines. The insured person as coinsurer pays the remainder.

Managed Care. Health care systems that integrate the financing and delivery of appropriate health care services to covered individuals by arrangements with selected providers to furnish a comprehensive set of health care services, explicit standards for selection of health care providers, formal programs for ongoing quality assurance and utilization review, and significant financial incentives for members to use providers and procedures associated with the plan.

Manual Rate. The premium rate developed for a group insurance coverage from the company's standard rate tables normally referred to as its rate manual or underwriting manual.

Medicaid. State programs of public assistance to persons regardless of age whose income and resources are insufficient to pay for health care. Title XIX of the federal Social Security Act provides matching federal funds for financing state Medicaid programs, effective January 1, 1966.

Medicare. The hospital insurance system and the supplementary medical insurance for the aged created by the 1965 amendments to the Social Security Act and operated under the provisions of the Act.

Medigap. A term sometimes applied to private insurance products that supplement Medicare insurance benefits.

Minimum Group. The least number of employees permitted under a state law to effect a group for insurance purposes; the purpose is to maintain some sort of proper division between individual policy insurance and the group forms.

Minimum Premium Plan (MPP). An arrangement under which an insurance carrier will, for a fee, handle the administration of claims and insure against large claims for a self-insured group.

Miscellaneous Expenses. Expenses in connection with hospital insurance, hospital charges other than room and board, such as X-rays, drugs, laboratory fees, and other ancillary charges. (Sometimes referred to as ancillary charges.)

Morbidity. The incidence and severity of sicknesses and accidents in a well-defined class or classes of persons.

Multiple Employer Trust (MET). A legal trust established by a plan sponsor that brings together a number of small, unrelated employers for the purpose of providing group medical coverage on an insured or self-funded basis.

National Association of Insurance Commissioners (NAIC). The association of insurance commissioners of various states formed to promote national uniformity in the regulation of insurance.

Noncancelable Guaranteed Renewable Policy. An individual policy which the insured person has the right to continue in force until a specified age, such as to age 65, by the timely payment of premiums. During this period, the insurer has no right to unilaterally make any changes in any provision of the policy while it is in force.

Noncontributory. A term applied to employee benefit plans under which the employer bears the full cost of the benefits for the employees. One hundred percent of the eligible employees must be insured.

Nondisabling Injury. An injury which may require medical care, but does not result in loss of working time or income.

Nonoccupational Policy. Contract which insures a person against off-the-job accident or sickness. It does not cover disability resulting from injury or sickness covered by Workers' Compensation. Group accident and sickness policies are frequently non-occupational.

Nonparticipating Insurance. Plan of insurance under which the policyholder is not entitled to share in the dividend distribution of the company.

Nonprofit Insurers. Persons organized under special state laws to provide hospital, medical, or dental insurance on a nonprofit basis. The laws exempt them from certain types of taxes.

Occupational Hazards. Occupations which expose the insured to greater than normal physical danger by the very nature of the work in which the insured is engaged, and the varying periods of absence from the occupation, due to the disability, that can be expected.

Optionally Renewable Contract. A contract of health insurance in which the insurer reserves the right to terminate the coverage at any anniversary or, in some cases, at any premium due date, but does not have the right to terminate coverage between such dates.

Overhead Insurance. A type of short-term disability income contract that reimburses the insured person for specified, fixed monthly expenses, normal and customary in the operation and conduct of his/her business or office.

Partial Disability. The result of an illness or injury which prevents an insured from performing one or more of the functions of his/her regular job.

Participating Insurance. Insurance issued by an insurance company providing participation in dividend distribution.

Physician's Expense Insurance. Coverage which provides benefits toward the cost of such services as doctor's fees for nonsurgical care in the hospital, at home or in a physician's office, and X-rays or laboratory tests performed outside the hospital. (Also called Regular Medical Expense Insurance.)

Point-of-Service Plans. Often known as open-ended HMOs or PPOs, these plans permit insureds to choose providers outside the plan yet are designed to encourage the use of network providers.

Policy. The legal document issued by the company to the policyholder, which outlines the conditions and terms of the insurance; also called the policy contract or the contract.

Policy Term. That period for which an insurance policy provides coverage.

Preadmission Certification. Process in which a health care professional evaluates an attending physician's request for a patient's admission to a hospital by using established medical criteria.

Preexisting Condition. A physical and/or mental condition of an insured which first manifested itself prior to the issuance of his/her policy or which existed prior to issuance and for which treatment was received.

Preferred Provider Organization (PPO). An arrangement whereby a third-party payer contracts with a group of medical care providers who furnish services at lower than usual fees in return for prompt payment and a certain volume of patients.

Premium. The periodic payment required to keep a policy in force.

Prepaid Group Practice Plan. A plan under which specified health services are rendered by participating physicians to an enrolled group of persons, with a fixed periodic payment in advance made by or on behalf of each person or family. If a health insurance carrier is involved, a contract to pay in advance for the full range of health services to which the insured is entitled under the terms of the health insurance contract. Such a plan is one form of Health Maintenance Organization (HMO).

Principal Sum. The amount payable in one sum in the event of accidental death and in, some cases, accidental dismemberment.

Professional Review Organization (PRO). An organization in which practicing physicians assume responsibility for reviewing the propriety and quality of health care services provided under Medicare and Medicaid.

Proration. The adjustment of benefits paid because of a mistake in the amount of the premiums paid or the existence of other insurance covering the same accident or disability.

Prospective Payment. An advancement of payment for health care charges that are likely to occur.

Qualified Impairment Insurance. A form of substandard or special class insurance, which restricts benefits for the insured person's particular condition.

Reasonable and Customary Charge. A charge for health care, which is consistent with the going rate or charge in a certain geographical area for identical or similar services.

Recurring Clause. A provision in some health insurance policies, which specifies a period of time during which the recurrence of a condition is considered a continuation of a prior period of disability or hospital confinement.

Rehabilitation. (1) Restoration of a totally disabled person to a meaningful occupation, (2) a provision in some long-term disability policies that provides for continuation of benefits or other financial assistance while a totally disabled insured is retraining or attempting to resume productive employment.

Reinstatement. The resumption of coverage under a policy which has lapsed.

Reinsurance. The acceptance by one or more insurers, called reinsurers, of a portion of the risk underwritten by another insurer who has contracted for the entire coverage.

Renewal. Continuance of coverage under a policy beyond its original term by the insurer's acceptance of the premium for a new policy term.

Residual Disability Benefits. A provision in an insurance policy that provides benefits in proportion to a reduction of earnings as a result of disability, as opposed to the inability to work full-time.

Rider. A document which amends the policy or certificate. It may increase or decrease benefits, waive the condition of coverage or in any other way amend the original contract.

Risk. Any chance of loss.

Self-Administration. The procedure where an employer maintains all records regarding the employees covered under a group insurance plan.

Self-Insurance. A program for providing group insurance with benefits financed entirely through the internal means of the policyholder, in place of purchasing coverage from commercial carriers.

Senior Citizen Policies. Contracts insuring persons 65 years of age or more. In most cases, these policies supplement the coverage afforded by the government under the Medicare program.

Short-Term Disability Income Insurance. The provision to pay benefits to a covered disabled person as long as he/she remains disabled up to a specified period not exceeding two years.

Social Security Freeze. A long-term disability policy provision which establishes that the offset from benefits paid by Social Security will not be changed regardless of subsequent changes in the Social Security law.

Special Risk Insurance. Coverage for risks or hazards of a special or unusual nature.

Standard Insurance. Insurance written on the basis of regular morbidity underwriting assumption used by an insurance company and issued at normal rates.

Standard Provision. Those contract provisions generally required by state statutes until superseded by the uniform policy provision.

Standard Risk. A person who, according to a company's underwriting standards, is entitled to insurance protection without extra rating or special restrictions.

State Disability Plan. A plan for accident and sickness, or disability insurance required by state legislation of those employers doing business in that particular state.

State Insurance Department. A department of a state government whose duty is to regulate the business of insurance and give the public information on insurance.

Substandard Insurance. Insurance issued with an extra premium or special restriction to those persons who do not qualify for insurance at standard rates.

Substandard Risk. An individual, who, because of health history or physical limitations, does not measure up to the qualification of a standard risk.

Surgical Expense Insurance. Health insurance policies, which provide benefits toward the physician's or surgeon's operating fees. Benefits may consist of scheduled amounts for each surgical procedure.

Surgical Schedule. A list of cash allowances attached to the policy, which are payable for various types of surgery, with a maximum amount based upon the severity of the operation.

Third-Party Administration. Administration of a group insurance plan by some person or firm other than the insurer or the policyholder.

Time Limit. The period of time during which a notice of claim or proof of loss must be filed.

Total Disability. An illness or injury which prevents an insured person from continuously performing every duty pertaining to his/her occupation or engaging in any other type of work. (This wording varies among insurance companies.)

Travel Accident Policy. A limited contract covering only accidents while an insured person is traveling, usually on a commercial carrier.

Unallocated Benefit. A policy provision providing reimbursement up to a maximum amount for the cost of all extra miscellaneous hospital services, but not specifying how much will be paid for each type of service.

Underwriter. The term as generally used applies to either (a) a company which receives the premiums and accepts responsibility for the fulfillment of the policy contract; (b) the company employee who decides whether or not the company should assume a particular risk; (c) the agent who sells the policy.

Underwriting. The process by which an insurer determines whether or not and on what basis an application for insurance will be accepted.

Unearned Premium. That portion of the paid premium applying to the unexpired portion of the policy term; or that portion of the paid premium for which protection has not been received.

Uninsurable Risk. One not acceptable for insurance due to excessive risk.

Waiting Period. The length of time an employee must wait from his/her date of employment or application for coverage, to the date his/her insurance is effective.

Waiver. An agreement attached to a policy which exempts from coverage certain disabilities or injuries which are normally covered by the policy.

Waiver of Premium. A provision included in some policies which exempts the policyholder from paying the premiums while an insured is totally disabled, during the life of the contract.

Workers' Compensation. Insurance against liability imposed on certain employers to pay benefits and furnish care to employees injured, and to pay benefits to dependents of employees killed in the course of or arising out of their employment.

Written Premiums. The entire amount of premiums due in a year for all policies issued by an insurance company.

INDEX